The Greatest Gift Guide Ever

The Greatest Gift Guide Ever

Judith King

BETTERWAY PUBLICATIONS, INC.

White Hall, Virginia

First Printing: September, 1982
Special Printing: May, 1986

Published by
Betterway Publications, Inc.
P.O. Box 70
White Hall, Virginia 22987

Cover Design by David Wagner
Illustrations by Robin Toth
Typography by Typecasting

Library of Congress Cataloging in Publication Data
King, Judith.
    The greatest gift guide ever.

    Includes index.
    1. Shopping.   2. Gifts—Catalogs.   I. Title
TX335.K434   1982   394   82–14682
    ISBN 0-932620-15-9 (pbk.)

Printed in the United States of America

Dedicated to
Fred, Tommy, and Sarah
for their patience and encouragement

Contents

Introduction 9

1. Helpful Hints for Gracious Giving 11
   Gift Shopping Guidelines
   Guide to Buying Toys
   Imaginative Wrapping Ideas
   When Gifts Must Be Mailed
   Creating a Gift Profile

2. Greatest Gift Ideas 21
   3200 gift ideas for 81 age and interest categories
   from Babies to Retirement Home Residents
   from Backpackers to Woodworkers

3. Special Interest Magazines 117
   The Gifts that Last all Year

4. Catalog Shopping from Your Armchair 133
   Where to find that *special* gift

5. Banish Gift Budget Blues with Things to Make 163
   Directions for gifts that children and adults can make

   Appendix 171
   Small Electric Appliances
   General Birthday Information
   Wedding Anniversary Symbols and Gift Ideas
   Gift Reminder Calendar

   Index 188

Introduction

How many times have you wanted to give someone a gift, but just could not think of anything appropriate—at least not in a price range you could afford? How often have you *needed* that perfect present for a treasured, but seldom seen, niece or nephew...a thoughtful gift for a handicapped person...a "just right" surprise for a hobbyist?

The Greatest Gift Guide Ever was compiled for **you**. The ideas in this book will stretch your imagination, respect your budget, make shopping fun and rewarding, and earn you a collection of **sincere** thank-you notes.

The book is full of ideas for interesting, useful gifts that are affordable on even the tightest budgets. I guarantee you will be able to find a gift that will be appreciated for everyone on your list.

Months of research—interview after interview—went into making this the best book possible. Innumerable gift suggestions were collected from specialty shops, department stores, catalogs, special interest magazines, and books. Hundreds of retail clerks recommended popular or clever gift items. Scores of persons involved in hobbies or special interest activities told me what gifts they would love to receive.

After the research was completed and the sorting and evaluating were done, more than 3,200 items were chosen for the book. Most of them cost less than $50. Some cost nothing more than a little time. In order to maintain our arbitrary $50 ceiling, we had to omit some large, obvious items; for example, a camera for a photographer or a microwave oven for a cook. If you have more than $50 to spend on a gift, your range of choices is almost unlimited. The challenge comes in finding something truly useful or appreciated—and a gift you will be proud to give—for under $50; for many gift-buyers, under $10.

For many reasons, prices for individual items have not been included. Not only do these vary by region and time of year, the size, quality and style of any item will influence its price. One extreme example: a potted plant could be a $30 *Ficus Benjamina* or a cutting from your flower bed, planted in a clay pot you have decorated.

Some gift categories list coupons for such activities as lawn mowing or babysitting. They can be index cards or pieces of paper given like an I.O.U. —a sort of promissory note—to be redeemed at a time convenient for both donor and recipient. These coupons are especially helpful in solving children's gift-giving problems when they want to furnish a gift but don't have the money to buy one.

Now, a few simple suggestions to help you use this book to save time, worry and gasoline:

First, turn to the "Gift Reminder Calendar" on page 175. Write down each birthday, anniversary or other recurring gift occasion you want to remember. Check this calendar often and use it year after year.

Next, read the section called *Creating A Gift Profile* (see page 17), and develop a gift profile for each person to whom you give regularly. Taking a few minutes to do it thoroughly now will save you time in the long run. Leave plenty of space to update each profile as individual interests change. Jot down ideas throughout the year. Be sure to record what you give each person so you won't duplicate in the future.

Next, look over each gift category applicable to your friends and members of your family and have fun selecting from the many gifts that will please them *and* your budget.

Many sections refer you to hundreds of magazines which people with that particular interest would enjoy. You also will find addresses for almost 500 specialty mail-order catalogs, which will expand your choice of merchandise significantly (and save you more time and gasoline). Many catalogs offer gift certificates, sometimes a handy idea if the recipient lives out of town.

The gifts you give do not have to be expensive or brightly wrapped to be appreciated. Remember that the ideas in this book came from many, many people with different interests and needs who would love to receive these gifts.

Happy giving!

Helpful Hints

Gift Shopping Guidelines
Guide to Buying Toys
Imaginative Wrapping Ideas
When Gifts Must Be Mailed
Creating a Gift Profile
Gift Profile Form

Gift Shopping Guidelines

Here are some tips to make gift giving easier and more enjoyable for you as well as those on your list.

• Fill in the Gift Calendar at the back of this book with the anniversaries, birthdays, and other annual events you want to remember. Consult it often, looking several weeks ahead so you won't be taken by surprise by a forgotten gift occasion.

• Jot down gift ideas as you think of them. As soon as possible, transfer them to your Gift Profile notebook (see page 17, *Creating A Gift Profile*).

• Buy to please the recipient's taste and style, not your own.

• Buy the quality of merchandise you would like to have.

• When you find a bargain, buy it even if you won't need the gift for several months.

• Keep a "gift box" of sale items on hand for a birthday party your child forgot until an hour before the party or as an unexpected "thank you."

• Shop early—especially if you are ordering from a catalog.

• Keep all receipts for at least three months in case an exchange is necessary.

• Keep an updated list of your family's sizes on a small card in your wallet so you can take advantage of unexpected sales or buy something that strikes you as "just right."

• If buying accessories (for camera, gun, sewing machine, etc.), find out the brand name and number of the main item to minimize exchanges.

• Try to find out the recipient's favorite brand (particularly on sporting or hobby equipment).

• Keep a list from year to year of gifts to family and friends so you won't duplicate.

Guide to Buying Toys

Use these guidelines to be sure the toys you give are safe and appropriate.

• The toy must be safe, well-made, and sturdy; i.e. non-toxic paint, smooth edges, and, on young children's toys, no parts that can be swallowed. Refrain from buying brittle plastic toys. They seem inexpensive, but don't last long. When broken, they produce sharp, cutting edges. Sturdy plastic, wood and metal toys may cost more, but they last proportionately longer.

• Electric toys (such as record players) for children under six (safe age varies with each child's maturity) usually should be battery powered. Be sure electrical toys carry the UL (Underwriters Laboratory) seal of approval. Include the required number and size of batteries with the toy as a special treat.

• Toys should be appropriate for the individual child. Some five-year-olds are fascinated by pocket calculators and some boys like dolls. The children I know have proved overwhelmingly that toys are not sexist, so I have not labeled anything *girls* or *boys*. When in doubt, save the sales receipt!

• Toys should be fun. Play is a child's "job." Through play he learns about his abilities, his emotions, and his interaction with others. If a toy is too advanced, the child will feel frustrated and inferior. Select a toy he can enjoy now, not one he'll grow into.

• A good toy requires a lot of imagination and interaction by the child. The robot that struts across the floor when wound may be fun for a few minutes, but will not add to a child's knowledge about himself. Pick something with which he can get involved.

• The younger the child, the simpler and bigger the toy should be to match the child's developmental stage.

• Just because a game or toy carries the name of a popular TV show or movie does not guarantee it will be a "wise" gift selection. Where possible, read the game rules to see if it sounds interesting or judge the toy on merits other than its name.

• Some toy manufacturers consistently produce good sturdy toys. Some I like are Mattel (Tuff Stuff), Fisher-Price, Creative Playthings, Tonka, Playskool, Matchbox, Sifo, Childcraft, and Lego. There are other equally reliable firms. Some perhaps are smaller and do not have national distribution. Some you may discover through the Toys & Games category in the Catalog Section of this book. If possible, ask mothers you know about favorite toys. It's more fun to give (and receive) a toy that will still be usable four months after the gift occasion.

• Teacher supply stores are good sources of gifts for children that are both educational and fun.

Imaginative Wrapping Ideas

- Wrap in brown or manila paper and let children color a picture on it.
- Sunday comics make colorful wrapping paper.
- Slip present into a fabric drawstring bag, which can be reused for gifts or used for overnights, storage, camper's laundry bag, etc.
- Tie girl's present with thick yarn to be used as hair ribbon.
- Tie teenager's or child's package with decorated shoelaces.
- Tie a surprise onto the box—a pencil for a teacher, a lollipop for a child, a potato peeler for a cook, a spatula for a bride, a screwdriver for a handyman.
- Wrap a box like a package, but put in it a slip of paper containing a "clue." That clue leads to the hidden present or to a string of clues. All ages love this one.
- Use plain paper and stamp "First Class" (from a rubber stamp used for mail) in colored ink all over.
- Make your own wrapping paper with potato or block print.
- Draw scenes on plain wrapping paper and glue on an inexpensive toy; (e.g., draw a road and glue on an inexpensive toy car.)
- Place gift in a pretty tin, wood, or plastic reusable box or glass jar.
- Put gift in clay flower pot, straw basket, stainless steel mixing bowl, toolbox, bucket or other container useful to the recipient and tie with ribbon.
- Wrap present in bandana, handkerchief, hand or dish towel.
- Draw a face on plain paper and use coins or round candies for eyes, small pocket comb for a toothy mouth, or wrapped sticks of gum for arms and legs.
- When giving gifts of food, it's a nice extra touch to put cookies on a pretty resuable tray or plate or wrap bread in foil and replace in (washed!) pan and tie with a ribbon.
- Instead of expensive greeting cards, use colorful stickers on unruled, colored index cards.
- Use scraps of fabric to wrap gifts or make bows from them and tape onto plain butcher's paper.
- Save bows year after year.
- Decorate packages with pinecones, acorns, sweet gum balls or other natural material.
- Reuse Christmas, birthday, or other occasion cards by cutting along the seam and discarding the signed part. Sign on the back, or glue onto the front of a package, or cut out parts of the picture to glue onto your package.

When Gifts Must Be Mailed

Containers:
- Padded mailing bags are fine for books, small objects that might get lost, and soft goods such as clothing.
- Paper board boxes are usually sufficient up to 10 pounds, but fiberboard boxes are better. Over 10 pounds, always use fiberboard.

Cushioning:
- Wrap fragile items individually with foamed plastic or padding. Set in box and fill box with popcorn or Styrofoam beads or wadded newspaper (packed tightly so contents do not shift around).
- Liquid items should be packed in double, leakproof containers, then treated as fragile items.
- Perishables should be packed in odorless absorbent packing material.
- Try to distribute the weight of the contents evenly over the box and pack tightly so contents do not move around during handling.

Sealing:
- Padded bags may be sealed with staples and reinforced with tape (not masking tape).
- Acceptable tapes are filament, strapping, waterproof, or pressure sensitive. The U.S. Postal Service will accept reinforced paper tape.
- Tape over the opening of the box. Then apply several rows of tape **across** the opening for additional protection.
- United Parcel Service will not accept packages with brown paper, string, or masking tape on the outside.

Addressing:
- Type a label or use permanent ink markers (so address will not easily smear). Or write in ink and cover address with several layers of transparent tape.
- Have only one address label on the outside, addressed like a letter.
- Be sure to include Zip codes.
- Write or type address and your return address on a piece of paper and put inside the box just in case the box is damaged and the address label lost or ruined.

Insurance:
The little you pay extra to insure a package is well worth the energy you will *not* waste worrying about its safe arrival.

UNITED PARCEL SERVICE MAILING REQUIREMENTS
They will accept any package up to 50 pounds and up to 108 inches (height and girth combined). There is no minimum, but they prefer no smaller than shoebox size. Padded mailers are acceptable if well insulated.

Packages may not have brown paper, string, or masking tape on the outside. Use strapping, waterproof, or pressure-sensitive tape.

Have only one address label on the outside, addressed like a letter.

DOMESTIC POSTAL INFORMATION

Size standards:

Minimum sizes: Pieces which do not meet the following requirements are prohibited from the mail:

    a. All pieces must be at least .007 inch thick and

    b. All pieces (except keys and identification devices) which are ½ inch or less thick must be:

        (1) Rectangular in shape

        (2) At least 3½ inches high and

        (3) At least 5 inches long.

    NOTE: Pieces greater than ¼ inch thick can be mailed even if they measure less than 3½ × 5 inches.

Non-Standard Mail: All First Class mail weighing 1 oz. or less and all single piece rate Third Class mail weighing 1 oz. or less is nonstandard (and subject to a 9-cent surcharge in addition to the applicable postage and fees) if:

    a. Any of the following dimensions are exceeded

        Length—11½ inches

        Height—6⅛ inches

        Thickness—¼ inch, or

    b. The piece has a height to length (aspect) ratio which does not fall between 1 to 1.3 and 1 to 2.5 inclusive. The aspect ratio is found by dividing the length by the height. If the answer is between 1.3 and 2.5 inclusive, the piece has a standard aspect ratio.

Rates: **(Use this chart to record current rates.)**

First Class: Post Card   _____

                Letter, first ounce   _____

                      Each additional ounce   _____

Second Class: (For individual copies of newspapers or periodicals)

                      First ounce   _____

                      2 ounces   _____

                      Each additional ounce up to 16 ounces   _____

                      Or the applicable Fourth Class rate, whichever is lower.

Third Class: (Circulars, books, catalogs, and other printed matter; merchandise, seeds, cuttings, bulbs, roots, scions, and plants, weighing less than 16 ounces.)

                      0–1 ounce   _____

                      Over 1 to 2 ounces   _____

                      Over 2 to 3 ounces   _____

                      Over 3 to 4 ounces   _____

                      Over 4 to 6 ounces   _____

                      Over 6 to 8 ounces   _____

                      Over 8 to 10 ounces   _____

                      Over 10 to 12 ounces   _____

                      Over 12 to 14 ounces   _____

                      Over 14 to 15.99 ounces   _____ *

* Or use Fourth Class rate (Parcel Post)—Consult postmaster for rates.

Creating a Gift Profile

Developing a gift profile is nothing more than writing down everything you notice about a person—his or her hobbies, work, interests, styles, details about her home, etc. When a gift-giving time nears, use this information to direct you to appropriate gift categories in this book. You will find a wide variety of pleasing gift ideas from which to choose.

You probably will want to organize a special notebook for your gift profiles. Or, you may want to make it easy on yourself and buy a special notebook, *My Personal Gift Profiles*. (See the order form in the back of this book.) Whether you buy the notebook or create your own, write the individual's name at the top of the page. Now begin listing everything you know about that person that could be a clue to a gift he or she would appreciate. When you run out of ideas, refer to the questions that follow. Add as much detailed information as possible. Update it as interests change.

Where does your information come from? From observing and listening. If you had trouble thinking of anything to write, then you need to train yourself to be observant and to listen. The next time you see the person, be aware of everything about him or her and try to find the answers to as many of the questions as you can. Make mental notes of the music he likes, the style of clothing she wears, or the topics each talks about. As soon as possible, write this in your profile notebook. Soon you automatically will pick up clues about a person that will be useful on gift occasions.

Here are some questions to ask yourself when making your gift profiles. They apply to anyone on your list regardless of sex or age.

1. Is he or she married? Are children or grandchildren an important part of his or her life? Will the gift be shared with a spouse or the family or given just to the individual?

2. How old is he? Does he have any physical impairments that would limit your gift choice or give you fresh ideas?

3. What kind of work does the individual do? Would he enjoy a useful or whimsical reminder of his work or would he prefer not to be reminded? In what organizations is he active?

4. What does she like to talk about: ecology, genealogy, music, cinema, traveling, politics, Hollywood trivia, sports, books, her job?

5. Does he have a favorite hobby or craft? What artistic endeavors does she pursue: needlework, decoupage, pottery, woodworking? Is he an amateur or professional? Does he collect knickknacks, collector's items or antiques? What subject or style?

6. What does she do in her spare time—play golf, sew, hunt, jog, garden, fish, watch television, build models, dance?

7. What games does he play—cards, board games, word games, crossword or jigsaw puzzles?

8. What was his alma mater? Or school he is now attending or hopes to attend? What is its mascot?

9. What special foods or drinks does she like? Does she like to eat out or cook in? Where? What kind of cooking or serving accessories could he use?

10. What kind of magazines or books does he have on his tables or in his bookshelves? What kind of music does he like? What kind of movies or plays does she attend? Is he interested in any spectator sport?

11. What tools or equipment does he borrow from you?

12. Does he travel or want to? To where: the beach, the mountains, overseas? By airplane, car, ship, bus? Does he camp out?

13. What are some possessions of which she is especially proud: a new car, her home, garden, antique organ, pet, stamp collection?

14. What style clothes does he wear or like: conservative, Western, the latest fashion? What are her colors: busy prints, mostly pastels, earth tones?

15. Does she wear jewelry, scarves, hair ornaments? Is her jewelry flashy, sophisticated, simple, gold or silver? Are her ears pierced? What size are her dresses, lingerie, blouses, gloves?

16. Does he wear jewelry, cuff links, tie tacks, sweaters? What size are his shirts, belts, gloves?

17. Does he have a favorite fragrance, flower, brand of toiletries or cosmetics, candy, author, singer or musician?

18. Does she like plants, records, knickknacks, wall decorations, home-made foods or items?

19. What style are his home furnishings: antique, early American, Spanish, Western, contemporary, eclectic? Or is he indifferent to home decorating and accessories?

20. What colors are in the kitchen, bathroom, bedroom, dining room, living room?

21. Does she have pets?

22. Does he smoke? Does he collect pipes? What kind of tobacco or cigars does he prefer?

23. Is he a formal or informal person? Sentimental or practical? Does she like surprises or jokes?

The list could go on and on. These questions, however, should stimulate your thinking about the person you want to remember. Pick out a few of his or her special interests. Turn to the corresponding gift categories and, with confidence, choose a present you **know** the recipient will like and appreciate.

Gift Profile

Gift Profile for _____

Birthday _____   **Birthstone** _____

Anniversary _____

Sizes

Blouse/Shirt _____   **Sweater** _____

Slacks (waist/length) _____   **Dress/Suit** _____

Belt _____   **Shoes** _____

Coat/Jacket _____   **Underwear** _____

Gloves _____   **Pajamas/Nightgown** _____

Hat _____   **Ring** _____

Favorites

Color _____

Kind of music _____

Singer/Entertainer _____

Kind of book _____

Author _____

Wine/Liquor _____

School _____

Sport/Team _____

Candy _____

Flower _____

Scent _____

Comments

Hobbies:

Profession or work area:

Topics of conversation:

Collections:

Home:

Things he/she has wished for:

Other observations:

Gift Ideas:

Gift Record

Date: **Item:**

_____   _____

_____   _____

_____   _____

_____   _____

_____   _____

_____   _____

_____   _____

_____   _____

Gift Ideas

Baby

1-Year Old

2-Year Old

3- to 5-Year Olds

6- to 10-Year Olds

11- to 14-Year Olds

15- to 18-Year Olds

Adult (Basic)

Anniversaries

Antique Collector

Artist

Bachelor

Backpacker

Bar Gifts

Bar Mitzvah or
   Bat Mitzvah

Boater

Bowler

Bridesmaid

Camper

Christmas Specials

Christmas Stocking
   Stuffers &
   Hanukkah Gifts

Clergy

Collector

College Graduation

College Student
   Away from Home

Cook

Crafts

Cyclist

Desk Dweller

Elderly at Own Home

Extra Special

Family

Farewell Gifts

Fireplace Gifts

Fisherman

Fitness Buff

Gardener

Golfer

Grandparents

Groomsman

Handicapped

Handyman

Hearing Impaired

High School
   Graduation

History Buff

Host / Hostess

Housewarming

Hunter

Ill Persons

Just a Little
   Something

Lefties

Men

Mentally Ill

Mentally Retarded

Musician

Needleworker

New Parents

Nursing Home
   Resident

Outdoors

Person Living Abroad

Photographer

Retirement Home
   Resident

Runner

Scuba Diver

Seamstress

Silver Gifts

Single Woman

Snow Skier

Sports Fan

Teacher

Tennis Player

Traveler

Vegetarian

Visually Impaired

Water Skier

Wedding

Wedding Showers

Western

Women

Wood Hobbyist

Writer

Baby

Probably most people have no trouble thinking of gift ideas for the first baby in a family, but when boy number three arrives, they begin to panic. This long list of baby gifts furnishes many new ideas. (See *Gift Ideas: New Parents* for a different slant on baby presents.)

Babies need anything to help them explore their senses—a variety of textures, sounds, shapes, and colors. Toys which encourage eye focus and hand-to-eye coordination are helpful. Be sure the toy has no small parts that can be torn off and swallowed. Washable toys are especially appreciated.

Major Equipment

Crib, crib bumpers, portable crib
Playpen, pad
High chair—collapsible with removable tray
Changing table, pad
Diaper bag with waterproof lining, compartments (Make one with Vogue pattern #8289.)
Bathtub, bathinette
Car seat with seat belts
Infant seat with several positions
Stroller—a collapsible one is especially nice.
Walker, bounce chair
Cool-mist humidifier, vaporizer
Baby swing for tree, doorway or on stand with a crank

Nursery Supplies

Fitted crib sheet, waterproof pads
Crib dust ruffle, canopy
Baby blanket—Receiving size or longer for child to grow into; washable quilt (might have friends or relatives embroider their names on the squares); crochet shell border around receiving blanket; sew two pieces of flannel together (with or without batting) and crochet shell border around them; bind 45 in. square of two-sided quilted material with wide bias tape.
Crib gym, crib activity box, mobile (maybe a musical one)
Nap roll
Hooded bath towels, baby washcloths
Diaper pail
Diaper stacker (Simplicity pattern #9751)
Paper diapers (even if Mom uses cloth, she'll need paper sometimes)
Baby clothes hangers
"Goody box" full of diaper pins, pin lubricator, blunt nail scissors, baby powder, baby lotion, creams, baby washcloths, bibs, waterproof pads, plastic pants, pacifier, rattle, etc.
Night light, nursery lamp
Personalized light switch plate
Wall hanging, picture to fit nursery theme

Feeding Accessories

Bottle sterilizer, bottles, bottle brush, nipples, bottle warmer
Weighted base-cup
Bibs
Shoulder burp pad
Portable baby seat that clamps to table (for restaurants)
Decorated dish set—plastic, stainless steel, or fine china
"Octopus" suction-cup plate holder (from dime store)
Food warming tray
Food mill or grinder
Baby-size eating utensils—silver or stainless

Some Old, Some New

Proof set of coins issued in year of birth
Commemorative stamps issued in year of birth
Newspaper from baby's birthplace on date of
    birth
Start or contribute to savings account in baby's
    name
Savings bond in baby's name
Baby book
Birth plaque—needlepoint, wooden, ceramic,
    etc.

Small picture frame
Paint colorful wall mural in nursery.
Pillow with music box (Buy a music box movement at a craft shop and insert
    into a handmade pillow or stuffed animal.)
Music box
Stuffed animal or doll (simple design, washable, no buttons!)
Sturdy, plastic toys that rattle or make noise (no sharp edges!), rubber squeeze
    toys
Baby bath toys
Rattle, pacifier, teething toys
Baby mirror (unbreakable)
Miscellaneous baby toys by Fisher-Price
Blocks—foam, plastic, or cardboard
Books—nursery rhymes, children's songs, cloth, or plastic with large pictures
    and ring binder, book in which main character shares baby's name
Birthday candle—marked for each birthday up to 18
Baby backpack, sling (Vogue pattern #8287)
Baby's travel mat and tote (Great idea from Simplicity pattern #9926.)
Padded lining for infant seat
Baby bracelet, ring, necklace
Silver teething ring, cup, bank
Make Christmas stocking or tree ornament with baby's name.
Clothes—bunting, diaper shirts, easy-off outfits, booties, bonnet; clothing
    up to one-year size is appreciated.

1-Year-Old

Toddlers need toys which give practice in hand-eye coordination and large muscle development. Toys in bright primary colors (red, yellow, and blue) help teach colors. Noisemakers (musical or not) are favorites. Watch out for small pieces that could choke a child. See *Catalogs: Toys & Games* for some sources.

Music box, musical toy, musical stuffed animal
Stuffed dolls, animals—washable! no buttons!
Big, soft ball
Toy telephone
Stacking toys, sorting toys
Hammering toys
Hard plastic people, animals, tools
Soft, rubber toys
Pull or push toys—especially ones that make noise

Bath toys, water play toys
Make a drawstring tub toy holder out of nylon net.
Simple train set
Small, sturdy cars, trucks, planes; big ones for outdoors
Sandbox and toys—pail, sifter, plastic bowls, shovel, etc.
Small tricycle, riding toy, rocking horse
Creative Coaster® (Fisher-Price)—wagon full of plastic blocks
Swing set, slide, Dome Climber® (Creative Playthings), Indoor Gym House® (Creative Playthings)
Blocks—cardboard, wood, plastic, cloth-covered foam, needlepoint
Books—cloth, plastic or cardboard pages; simple pictures or stories; nursery rhymes; *Best Word Book Ever,* Richard Scarry (Golden Press, 1963).
Toy chest, shelves
Non-tip step stool
Child's chair
Picture or stitchery for room
Height chart for wall
Personalized light switch plate
Child's dishes, silverware, cup with cartoon or storybook design
Clothes, overalls, mittens
Child's dishes, silverware, cup with cartoon or storybook design
Clothes, overalls, mittens
Jewelry—necklace, bracelet, hair barrettes
Personalized Christmas tree ornament
Add to savings account; buy savings bond.
Waterbaby swimming classes at YWCA or YMCA
Enlarge baby's picture or give coupon to have portrait made.

2-Year-Old

The two-year-old's immediate concern on gift occasions is tearing open the packages. What's inside is secondary. So wrap presents in as many different packages as possible! Still watch for small parts that can choke a child. Items that encourage independence and curiosity are appropriate (as if a two-year-old needs encouragement in these areas!) See *Catalogs: Toys & Games* for some sources.

Indoor Gym House® (Creative Playthings) or Toddler's Gym (Childcraft)
Creative Coaster® (Fisher-Price)—wagon full of plastic blocks
Blocks—wood, hollow cardboard, plastic
Preschool Lego®, interlocking blocks
Small metal, wooden, or tough plastic cars, trucks, trains, airplanes
Fisher-Price Circus Train, Village, Farm, Nursery School, etc.
Hard plastic people (astronauts, cowboys, etc.) and animals (dinosaurs,
    domestic, horses)
Plastic tools
Sorting toys
Snap-together toys, stacking toys—
    large plastic or wooden pieces
Very simple puzzles—wooden with a
    few big pieces
Large wooden beads to string
Toy telephone
Close and play record player (*not* plug-
    in type), Fisher-Price Music Box-
    Record Player

Rhythm instruments, musical toys, xylophone, drum
Balls, balloons
Outdoor equipment—slide, swing set, Dome Climber® (Creative Playthings),
    jungle gym, sandbox, tricycle, wagon, a riding toy; large metal trucks, con-
    struction equipment, cars; sturdy shovel or spoon, bowls, sifter, funnel,
    empty plastic bottles, cups, pail; innertube, arm float-supports for super-
    vised swimming
Books—picture book, nursery rhymes, one with character of same name as
    child, counting books, alphabet book (Make one from McCall's pattern
    #7524.), labeling book such as *Best Word Book Ever,* Richard Scarry
    (Golden Press, 1963)
Cloth book or doll teaching fastening (Vogue pattern #1959) or large clown
    doll with all kinds of fasteners (Butterick pattern #3510)
Dolls—large, cuddly, soft, easy to handle and to love (for boys, too!)
Large-size doll furniture, buggy, bed
Small suitcase, tote bag
Costumes, big clothes, purse, etc. for make-believe or dress-up
Stick horse (Simplicity pattern #7744)
Jewelry—rings, bracelet, necklace, beads, pins
Unbreakable polished steel mirror (Creative Playthings)

Mittens, caps, poncho, other clothes
Play dishes—unbreakable plastic or metal
Junior silverware, dishes, cup in decorative pattern (Sesame Street, Muppet, and Disney characters are favorites.)
Small size chair, table
Toy chest, shelves
Picture, monogram, stitchery for room
Light switch extender (helps child turn lights on)
Step-stool for bathroom
Bath toys, terry cloth hand mitt or puppet
Bubble bath
Decorative toothbrush
Cartoon or personalized bath towel, sheets, pillowcases, beach towel
Afghan, quilt
Personalized or unbreakable Christmas tree ornament
Add to savings account; buy savings bond.
Waterbaby swimming class at YMCA or YWCA

3- to 5-Year-Olds

While toys that teach hand-to-eye coordination and muscle development still are very important during these years, children are now able to enjoy mind-stretching toys, too—puzzles, art supplies, and building toys.

Transportation toys, role-play equipment, and simple science, math, and language skills toys are appropriate. Remember that toys know no sex so if a boy wants a necklace or a girl wants a tractor, please oblige.

Special interests and abilities vary so much that some gifts from the 2-Year-Old list and some from the 6- to 10-Year Old list may be appropriate for the child you have in mind. See *Catalogs: Toys & Games.*

For party, hire clown or magician or rent movie (see *Catalogs: Movies,* or check with local library.)
Trip to circus, zoo, ice show, rodeo, amusement park, carnival, child's movie, child's favorite eating place (be prepared for hamburgers!), ballet, ball-game, fire station, bakery, farm or city (whichever is *not* where he lives)
Ride on airplane, train, boat, etc.
Lessons in swimming, dancing, tumbling, sport, etc.
Art supplies—blunt scissors, crayons, chalk, felt tip pens, paper (white and colored), finger paint, Play Doh® (or see *Things to Make: Cooked Play Dough* for recipe), clay, paste, tablet, coloring books, pencils (personalized), old catalogs to cut up
Activity books
Books by Dr. Seuss, Richard Scarry, Mercer Mayer, Bill Peet; "Madeline" books by Ludwig Bemelmans; "Berenstain Bear" books by Stan Berenstain are particularly good as are *A Monster is Coming,* Florence Parry Heide & Roxanne Heide (Franklin Watts, 1980); *Where the Wild Things Are,* Maurice Sendak (Harper & Row, 1963) and other of his books

Books—alphabet, counting, labeling books; simple stories, beginning diction-
  aries, easy-to-read; nature; nursery rhymes; fairy tales
Bookmark, bookends
Magazine subscription (see *Magazines: Children*)
Blackboard, bulletin board; magnetic board with letters, numbers
Record player—close and play (mature 5-year-olds might be ready for the plug-
  in kind.)
Records—especially those with read-along books
View Master® and reels
Board games (requiring no reading, but using identification and counting) such
  as Candyland® or Chutes & Ladders® (both Milton Bradley)
Matching games—playing cards, Old Maid, Lotto®, dominoes
Sewing cards
Craft sticks or Popsicle sticks for craft projects
Favorite characters are from Sesame Street, Disney, Muppets, Star Wars and
  Empire Strikes Back. Girls love Strawberry Shortcake™ and friends.

Outdoor Play Equipment

Swing set, Jungle Gym, slide, rope ladder, tire swing
Tricycle, bicycle (with training wheels for beginner), bicycle license plate with
  child's name, wagon, scooter, sled, toboggan
Skates—kind without ball bearing wheels for first roller skates; ice skates
Stilts (see *Things to Make*)
Construction vehicles, cranes, trucks, cars
Wading pool, inflatable water toys, pail, water toys
Beginning sports equipment—balls of all kinds, ¾ or junior size basketball,
  large plastic ball and bat, Frisbee®
Playhouse—It does not have to be a work of art. A child would love to get
  the wood, cardboard or whatever and build it himself.
Outdoor drinking faucet—attaches to outdoor faucet

Role-Play Toys

Dolls—all sizes, kinds; baby dolls; Sunshine Family®, Barbie® (Mattel) dolls;
  space character dolls, e.g. from Star Wars; Muppets, Strawberry Short-
  cake™ and friends. Don't overlook dolls for boys.
Flip-over dolls (Little Red Riding Hood on one end, the wolf on the other—
  Butterick pattern #4150; Goldilocks and a bear—Butterick pattern #4149).
Doll accessories—furniture, clothes, house, buggy
Paper dolls (see *Things to Make: No Sew Doll*)
Doll or pillow with zipper, buttons, laces, snaps
Playskool's Dressy Bessy® or Butterick pattern #3510 is a delightful clown.
Small-scale household items—kitchen appliances, apron, mop, broom, tea set,
  dishes, etc. Fisher-Price has several sturdy sets.
Mattel Tuff Stuff®—indestructible vacuum cleaner, drill, mixer, etc.

Tools—Depending on child, you can introduce real hammer, nails, box of scrap wood, tool box, wrench, screwdriver, etc.; heavy plastic tools are still appropriate.

Hand puppets, finger puppets, puppet stage, puppet curtain (see *Things to Make*)

Costumes—old clothes, purse, costume jewelry, shoes; or ready-made outfits for cowboy, Indian, astronaut, dancer, princess, etc.; bandana

Hats—cowboy, Indian headdress, football helmet, crown (cardboard covered with aluminum foil with sequins glued on), fireman, baseball, space helmet

Teepee—Make it with 3 dowel sticks and circle of cloth.

Cardtable house (see *Things to Make*)

Stick horse (Simplicity pattern #7744)

Other Toys

Transportation toys—any size train set, cars, airplanes, spaceship, trucks, cranes, tractors

Construction set—blocks, Lego®, Bristle Blocks™ (Playskool), Brix Blox™ (Sears), Tinkertoy®, Lincoln Logs®, other interlocking block sets

Giant Tinkertoy® Construction Set

Small hard plastic or wooden people, animals

Space toys—dolls, sword, helmet, cape, spaceship; Star Wars™, Empire Strikes Back™ or Star Trek™ toys.

Nerf® toys—foam

Balloons—can fill with gum, pencils, coins, barrettes, etc.

Bath colors, bath toys, terry cloth puppet

Bubble gum machine

Trinket box

Music box

Musical instrument—piano, xylophone, tambourine, drum, Fisher-Price Marching Band

Cookie cutter assortment

Popsicle forms

Simple Science Toys

Silly Putty®

Slinky®

Flashlight

Magnifying glass—Mounted kind is nice.

Magnet, magnetic fishing pole (see *Things to Make* for directions)

Ant farm

Kaleidoscope

Calculators—Little Professor®, Quiz Kid® (both Texas Instruments) or inexpensive pocket kind for 5-year-olds

Toy clock

Cuisenaire Rods®—for learning math concepts

Bug House

For Child's Room

Small table, chairs, rocking chair, bean bag chair, book shelf

Decorative wastebasket

For walls—long mirror, stitchery, picture, monogram, growth chart, personalized light switch plate, framed pictures of relatives (hang low), calendar with pictures of interest to child, empty picture frame for child's art

Linens—afghan, quilt; bedspread, sheets, pillowcases in cartoon, space, fairy tale, children's design

Throw pillow

Slumber bag for overnights—Vogue pattern #1941 has full-size toss rugs of jungle animals; snug sack™

Tooth-fairy pillow—small pillow with small pocket attached to hold tooth and surprise from tooth fairy

Holiday decorations

Personal

Fancy comb, brush, hand mirror (see *Things to Make: Child's Mirror*)

Barrettes (see *Things to Make: Ruffled Barrettes*)

Hair ribbons (Make a palette of colored ribbons by winding 24-inch-long pieces of several colors around a cardboard rectangle.)

Little purse, suitcase

Drawstring totebag with child's name; real suitcase

Pretend make-up

Children's jewelry—necklace, bracelet, rings (Do not overlook decoder and "hero" rings for boys and girls.) Personalized items are nice.

Clothes—especially mittens, cap, pajamas with cartoon or sport or movie theme, T-shirt, belt, anything personalized

Personalized or funny placemat, mug, dishes, bath towel, beach towel, Christmas tree ornament

Make a child's telephone book (see *Things to Make*)

Penny bank, coins, dollar bill

Lunch kit

Wooden, felt, cloth nativity set child can play with

6- to 1O-Year-Olds

Children in this age bracket can handle construction sets, beginning sports and musical equipment, games requiring strategy and social interaction, and toys that require physical exertion. They are also developing interests in simple crafts, fads, and science. See *Catalogs: Craft Supplies, Science, Toys & Games, Books, Indian Supplies, Models & Miniatures.*

Hire a clown, magician, or storyteller for a party.

Rent a cartoon or special movie for a party (see *Catalogs: Movies*), or check with your local library.

Trip to circus, movie, ball game, ballet, rodeo, carnival, historical monument, museum, favorite restaurant, etc. Let child take one or two friends if possible.

Ride on plane, train, boat to some special place.

Book of passes to movie, bowling alley, or skating rink or coupons to ice cream parlor or fast food restaurant

Lessons in swimming, gymnastics, ballet, karate, art, sport, musical instrument, etc.

Pet (with parental permission)

Add to savings account; savings bond

Toys That Can Teach

Record player, records, record holder; tape player or recorder, tapes

Magazine subscription (see *Magazines: Children*)

Children's encyclopedia

Books on sports, science, nature, fiction, simple biographies, beginning dictionary, fairy tales, animals, comic books, mysteries, space

The following series books are well-liked: *Choose Your Own Adventure, Encyclopedia Brown, Chronicles of Narnia* (C. S. Lewis), *Little House on the Prairie* (Laura Ingalls Wilder), *Amelia Bedelia* (Peggy Parish), National Geographic Society's *Books for World Explorers* (beautiful photography), *Which Way* books, and mysteries such as Nancy Drew, Hardy Boys, Trixie Belden, Bobsey Twins, Tom Swift, Alfred Hitchcock and the Three Investigators, Judy Bolton, books by Wolfgang Ecke.

Other popular authors are Beverly Cleary, Bill Peet, and Shel Silverstein (especially *The Giving Tree,* Harper & Row, 1964).

Free Stuff for Kids, Pat Blakely et al. (Meadowbrook Press, 1979)

Bookends, bookmark, bookplates

Globe

Calculator, pocket or Texas Instruments' Quiz Kid®, Little Professor®

Child's Telephone Book (see *Things to Make*), address book

Begin a collection of stamps, coins, rocks, shells, baseball cards, post cards

Games—horseshoes, safe darts, ring toss, tether ball, badminton, racquet ball, croquet, volleyball, board games on reading level of child (or make your own on cardboard or plywood), simple card games, checkers, chess (see *Things to Make*), dominoes, bingo, Nerf™ Ping Pong

Some favorite games are Uno®, Connect Four®, Risk®, Yahtzee®, Clue®, Boggle®, Monopoly®, Chinese checkers, Parcheesi®, Speak & Spell™, Speak & Read™, Speak & Math™, Simon™, Rubik's Cube™

Jigsaw puzzles—have one made from child's photograph.

Outdoor Toys

Roller skates, ice skates, skating skirt

Bicycle, carrier rack, chain lock, reflective pedals, basket (see *Catalogs: Cycling* for motocross accessories)

Scooter

Skateboard, helmet, protective gear

Pogo stick, jumping shoes, stilts (see *Things to Make* for directions)
Sports equipment—baseball (batting trainer, glove, bat); basketball (junior size
for 6–7 year olds), hoop, backboard; soccer ball; tennis gear (see *Gift Ideas:
Tennis*); football (helmet, pads); see also *Gift
Ideas: Sports Fan*
Baton
Jacks, jump rope
Water toys—inflatables, rafts, beach ball, beach
towel, weighted diving rings
Yo-yo
Frisbee®
Kites
Clubhouse or material to make one (see *Things
to Make*)
Bug house, butterfly net, insect mounting kit

Creative Toys
Activity books—dot-to-dot, mazes, word puzzles
Art supplies—(personalized) pencils, eraser, tape, stapler, paper clips, crayons,
felt tip markers, paper, coloring books, rubber bands, scissors, glue, string,
label maker, etc.
Pencil sharpener
Paint-by-number kits
Snap-together models of cars, airplanes
Magic set
Sewing machine (play size)
Boy Scout craft kits (for boys and girls)
Crafts for 8 years and up—potter's wheel, candle making, string art, leather-
craft, glass cutting, needlework, shrink-art, birdhouse kit, weaving, wood
burning, printing, etc. Select kit by age printed on kit and maturity of
child.
Tools—nails, screws, hammer, screwdriver, handsaw, toolbox, hand drill, ruler
Power Shop (Mattel)
Science kits, microscope, telescope, crystal radio, etc.
Construction sets—Erector®, Construct-o-Straws® (Parker Bros.), Lego®, Brix
Blox™ (Sears), Riviton®, Lincoln Logs®
Children's cookbook, apron, miniature pans
Craft sticks or Popsicle sticks for crafts
838 Ways to Amuse a Child, June Johnson (Macmillan, 1962)
Kaleidoscope or octascope (reshapes the world outside)

For Child's Room
Desk, desk light
Clock, radio
Blackboard, bulletin board
Posters, wall mirror, needlework or decoupaged plaque or picture
Beanbag chair

Throw pillow (initial), fancy bed linens, quilt, slumber bag for slumber parties (Vogue pattern #2360)

Tooth fairy pillow—pillow with small outside pocket to hold tooth and surprise from tooth fairy

Type case or shelves for miniatures, treasures

Picture calendar

Holiday decorations

Other Toys, Gifts

Current fads are Smurf™, Strawberry Shortcake™ and friends (Apple Dumpling, Blueberry Tart, and other "delicious" dolls), Pac-man®, Annie™, Star Wars™, Empire Strikes Back™, Star Trek™, and E.T. Of course Snoopy, Walt Disney characters and the Muppets™ (Kermit and Miss Piggy) are still popular.

Stickers—Special varieties are puffies, googlie eyes (moving eyes) and smellies (scented)

Racing car set; small cars, trucks, vehicles, airplanes, trains; spaceships

Small people, animals—Playmobil Systems have many good sets (Indians, knights, construction workers, etc.)

Dolls, doll house and accessories, clothes, collector dolls, Barbie® and Strawberry Shortcake™ are popular.

Paper dolls (see *Things to Make: No-Sew Doll*)

Stuffed animals

Walkie-talkie

Flashlight

Cartoons to be shown on movie projector

Scrapbook, photograph album

Inexpensive camera, film

Penny bank, cash; raise child's allowance (or start one!)

Suitcase or tote bag for overnights, ballet or gymnastics lessons.

Satchel, backpack for school

Lunch kit

Fancy comb, brush set; hand mirror, hair ribbons; barrettes (see *Things to Make: Ruffled Barrettes*)

Watch

Jewelry (especially personalized)—ring, necklace, bracelet, pin

Jewelry box

Decorative tin or ceramic boxes for trinkets

Music box

Clothing—jean's belt, funny T-shirt, anything personalized, sweater, pajamas, nightgown, fancy socks, tights, jogging shorts, etc.

Personalized or funny place mat, mug, glass

Items with Boy or Girl Scout emblem (if child is a Scout)

Model train set—track, cars, engines, power pack, side buildings (kits to make), landscaping items

Video game program or home computer command module

11- to 14-Year-Olds

From about eleven years up, children like to experiment with various crafts, hobbies, sports, or scientific activities and eventually settle on three or four favorites. More complex, challenging games and toys are needed, depending of course on the child's skill level. See *Catalogs: Books, Craft Supplies, Models & Miniatures, Science, Toys & Games* for sources.

Tickets for bowling, miniature golf, roller or ice skating, sporting event, performing arts group, amusement park, movie, etc.

Take a few friends to swimming pool, movie, pizza parlor, skating rink, museum, etc.

Lessons in dance, art, musical instrument, sport, gymnastics, sewing, swimming, karate, woodworking, drama, etc.

Tuition in babysitting, first aid course

Pet (with parent's permission)

Magazine subscription (see *Magazines: Children*)

Books—biographies, science, fiction, mystery (Hardy Boys or Nancy Drew, encyclopedia, comic books, romance, adventure, sports, etiquette, babysitting, dictionary, hobby how-to, history)

The Baby-sitter's Handbook, Barbara Benton (William Morrow & Co., 1981)

Naturally It's Good...I cooked it myself!, Robin Toth (Betterway Publications, 1982)

Official Kids' Survival Kit, Elaine Chaback (Little Brown & Co., 1981)

The Giving Tree, Shel Silverstein (Harper & Row, 1964)

How to Master Home Video Games, Tom Hirschfeld (Bantam Books, 1982); *How to Master Video Games,* Tom Hirschfeld (Bantam Books, 1981)

Bookends, bookplates, bookmark, bookshelf

Child's own card at public library

Record player, records, record holder, stereo

Tape recorder, tape player, tapes, tape holder

Pocket calculator

Especially For Teens

Own telephone extension or line, decorator telephone

Radio, clock-radio, clock

Bulletin board

Autograph book, diary, pillow, animal

Address book, stationery, telephone book

Scrapbook, photograph album

Scratch 'n Sniff spiral notebooks

Wall posters of singers, movie personalities, slogans

Creative Gifts

Camera, film

Erector®, Lego® and other construction sets

Models of airplanes, cars, ships

Art kits, Doodle Art® posters, calligraphy kit

Craft kits—rock tumbling, stitchery, wood burning, macramé, sand painting, printing, ceramics, decoupage, weaving, shrink-art, etc.

Science kits—crystal radio, microscope, telescope, chemistry lab, etc.

Sewing machine, basket, equipment (see *Gift Ideas: Seamstress*)

Kit to make Christmas ornaments

Model train set—track, cars, side buildings (kits to make them), engines, power pack, bridges, landscaping accessories

Just for Fun

Skateboard, protective gear

Bicycle, carrier rack, basket, reflector pedals, motocross equipment (see *Gift Ideas: Cyclist*)

Sports equipment—baseball batter training set, throwback net, glove, bat; football, helmet; soccer or basketball (backboard, hoop); T-shirt, cap, notebook with favorite team's logo

Frisbee®, yo-yo, kite, darts, table tennis, Nerf™ Ping Pong®

Beach towel, beach ball, inflatable raft or floats, sun hat, weighted diving rings

Small cars, miniatures (soldiers or doll house collectibles)

Space toys, spaceships, stuffed animals

Yahtzee™, Scrabble™, Boggle™, Payday™, Risk®, Spill & Spell®, other board games, checkers, chess, card games, dominoes, table games

Pac-man® on T-shirts, watch, notebook, etc.

Battery-operated games, computer games, video games

Outdoor games—croquet, volleyball, ring toss, archery, horseshoes, badminton (see *Gift Ideas: Tennis*)

Jigsaw puzzles

For Room

Throw pillows—initials, personalized, shapes like seashell or butterfly

Sleeping bag for slumber parties

Beanbag chair

Trinket box, penny bank

Pictures, wall hangings, wall mirror, hand mirror

Teen bed or bath linens

Small potted plant

Type case or shadow box for miniatures, treasures

Music box

Slightly Personal

Funny T-shirt

Almost anything personalized—purse, pencils, jewelry, plaque, memo pads

Jewelry—ID bracelet, locket, earrings, small gold neck chain, anklet, chain bracelet, watch

Wallet, purse, key ring

Clothes—especially gowns, pajamas, jeans, T-shirt in disco colors, tube top, camisole top

Items with Boy or Girl Scout emblem (if child is a Scout)

Christmas tree ornament

15- to 18-Year-Olds

Many ideas for this in-between age group can come from special interest categories or *Adult (Basic)*.

Cash
Open savings account for him or her
Behind-the-wheel driving course
Course or book on babysitting, auto repair
The Baby-sitter's Handbook, Barbara Benton (William Morrow & Co., 1981).
Pet (with parent's permission)
Lessons in person's interest area—dance, bridge, photography, music, sports, crafts, sewing, art, karate, ceramics, etc.
Book of tickets to movie, miniature golf, amusement park, bowling alley, ice cream parlor, fast food restaurants
Two tickets to sports event, ballet, movie, entertainment event
Gift certificate to favorite clothing or craft store, restaurant (enough to take a date)

Especially for Teens

Amagift—album of over 40 gifts for teens from which recipient can choose; from local Amway distributors.
Key chain for new privilege of car keys
Stuffed animal
Spiral notebooks with sport figure, entertainer, rainbow, or popular slogan on cover
Diary, address book
Autograph book, pillow, animal
Scrapbook, photograph album
Gift certificate to favorite hairdresser
Own telephone line or extension, decorator telephone
Posters of entertainers, singers, slogans
Radio—electric, portable, or headphone
Stereo, record player, records, record stand
Tape player, tape recorder, tapes (blank or music), tape holder or carrier
Earphones or headphones for tape player, stereo, radio
Tank of gas

Just for Fun

Magazine subscription (see *Magazines: Children* or area of interest in magazine section)
Magazine rack
Books on famous people, sports or sports figures, young love, mystery, growing up, etiquette, adult development, science, adventure stories
Begin or add to collection—stamps, thimbles, coins

Jigsaw puzzles, crossword puzzle books
Rubik's Cube™, Missing Link™, Pyraminx™
Simple Solution to the Rubik's Cube, James G. Nourse (Bantam Books, 1981)
Table games such as chess (see *Things to Make: Nuts-and-Bolts-of-Chess Set*),
    checkers, cards, Michigan Rummy, Yahtzee™, Scrabble™
Outdoor games like volleyball, badminton, Frisbee®
Battery-operated games, computer games, video game
Hobby equipment, tools
Sports equipment for football, tennis, baseball, etc.
Bicycle, skateboard, accessories (see *Gift Ideas: Cyclist*)
Beach towel, beach ball, inflatable raft, beach umbrella
Small ice chest, Thermos®

Other Gifts
Type case or shelves for treasures
Bio-rhythm charts or kit
Stationery
Desk or drawer organizer, pen or pencil holder
Pen and pencil set
Personalized clip board
Typewriter, calculator
Bulletin board
Wall or hand mirror
Beanbag chair
Teen bed or bath linens—sports, romantic, nature themes
Personalized or handmade throw pillows, quilt, afghan, wall hanging or pic-
    ture or kit to make any of these
Craft, science kits such as needlework, wood burning, macramé, models, pom-
    pom craft, transistor radio kit, digital computer kit
Sewing machine, equipment (see *Gift Ideas: Seamstress*)
Clothes—especially disco colors, jeans, belts, T-shirt, nightgowns
Sachet
Jewelry box; decorative tin, wood, or ceramic box for trinkets
Jewelry—personalized, locket, earrings, small gold neck chain, bracelet, stick-
    pin, pendant, watch
Cosmetics, cologne
Hair dryer or other personal care appliance (see *Appendix: Small Electric
    Appliances*)
Wallet (how about a surprise inside?), purse, tote bag
Camera, film
Alarm clock, clock, clock radio
Potted plant for room
Luggage

Adult (Basic)

The following basic gift list is not meant to be complete. It is offered to help you with gifts for people you don't know well and also to avoid repeating some gift ideas in several categories. See also *Gift Ideas: Men, Women, Family, Bachelor, Single Woman,* and other interest categories.

See *Catalogs: Gifts* and *Smorgasbord* for sources for these and other gifts.

Tuition in defensive driving course

Tuition for a leisure course—yoga, quilting, rock climbing, photography, disco dancing, gourmet cooking, etc.

Anything you make well—needlepoint eyeglass case, macramé plant hanger, wooden trivet, etc.

Installation and several months of special telephone service—call waiting, call forwarding, three-way calling, speed calling

Telephone silencer, decorator telephone, gift certificate from phone company

Personalized bumper sticker or car license plates

Offer to inventory household goods for insurance (and take snapshots of valuable items and furniture).

Membership in local educational television station—Find out what amount entitles recipient to receive monthly program listing.

Rent a movie for a party or buy a copy of his favorite film (see *Catalogs: Movies*).

For 80th and subsequent birthdays, request a card from your mayor, governor or the President. Write four weeks in advance to Greetings Office, The White House, Washington, D. C. 20500. Include the recipient's full name, address, Zip code and month, day and year of birth.

Take him/her out to dinner, show, or entertainment event.

Tickets to sports event, opera, theater, bowling alley, etc.

Book of car wash coupons

Locking gas cap (for car)

Coupons for chores—lawn mowing, mending, weeding flower beds, etc.

Items relating to profession or hobby—tools, magazines, books, miniatures, needlepoint plaques, etc.

Call long distance; send a taped letter.

Singing telegram (see *Gift Ideas: Extra Special*)

Book on adult development, money management, how-to, time management

Family genealogy chart or book

Always Appropriate

Wallet, key case or ring

Automatic or folding umbrella

Magazine rack, record stand

Book (Garfield books are fun), record, magazine subscription, tape

The Greatest Gift Guide Ever

Bookends, bookmark (make one), bookplates

Desk calendar, pencil or pen holder, paperweight, memo board, desk accessories, letter holder

Briefcase, attaché case

Toll-Free Digest, (Warner Books, 1979) Directory of over 17,000 toll-free telephone listings.

Exercise bicycle or other exercise equipment (see *Gift Ideas: Fitness Buff*)

Membership in local spa or health club

Organizers for desk, belts, shoes, ties

Stationery

Gift certificate to favorite store or specialty shop or catalog

Amagift—albums of over 40 gifts in your selected price range from which recipient chooses, from local Amway distributors.

Terrarium, flowers, potted plant, hanging basket

Large-number, outdoor thermometer

Digital thermometer (for taking person's temperature)

Radio, CB, cassette recorder or player, alarm clock, clock radio

TV, video game program, command module for home computer

Pocket calculator, calculator game book

Watch

Nut cracker, package of nuts

Homemade goodies to eat

Food box, ham, turkey, liquor, wine, basket of fruit or cheese

Luggage, tote bags

Enlarge a favorite picture; have old pictures copied or restored.

Photograph album, camera, film

Board or table game—checkers, chess, backgammon, Michigan Rummy, Scrabble™

Outdoor game—croquet, Frisbee®, horseshoes, badminton

Playing cards, jigsaw puzzles (Put pieces in jar and keep the box!)

Brain teaser puzzle, Rubik's Cube™ or book on solving it

Decorative candle

Throw pillow (stitchery, needlepoint, letter-shaped)

Linens for bed, bath, or table

Popcorn popper, ice cream maker, etc. (see *Appendix: Small Electric Appliances*)

Sew hanging bags for shoes, dresses (Vogue pattern #8317)

Personal Items

Bath sheet—large wrap-around towel

Driving gloves

Scarves, neckscarf

Clothing—shirt, blouse, night clothes, robe, belt, sweater

Cosmetics—bath powder, bath oil, cologne, perfume, nail polish, after-shave lotion, any product in her favorite brand

Jewelry—ring, earrings, bracelet, neck chain, pendant, stick pin, pin; jewelry
   box or valet
Manicure set
Shower massage
Bio-rhythm chart or kit
Memory box—shadow box filled with meaningful miniatures or treasures
Picture of family for office or desk or wallet
Personal care appliance—see *Appendix: Small Electric Appliances*
Write a poem or song.
T-shirt or mug with special slogan, college logo or crest, or person's name
Flowers (yes, for a man, too), candy (unless she's dieting)

Anniversaries

For most anniversary ideas, you will want to refer to a hobby category or *Gift Ideas: Adult (Basic), Men, Women,* or *Wedding.* However, some anniversaries, like the 25th or 50th, call for something extra special. Actually with the soaring divorce rate, *any* anniversary is worth celebrating in a special way.

Many shops carry plates, vases, cups and saucers inscribed with "25th Anniversary." Perhaps that fits the taste of the couple you have in mind. But several wives I know who are on their second 25 wedded years whispered to me almost apologetically, "Put in your book, 'NOTHING ELSE TO DUST.'" So here are some ideas that I hope will add to the couple's happy memories. See also *Appendix: Wedding Anniversaries.*

Make a scrapbook of family photos, letters, or
   remembrances.
Make a family quilt with each family member
   making a square. Children can draw with
   permanent ink markers.
Family photograph
Composite picture frame filled with family
   photos
Enlarge and frame a favorite photograph.
Picture frame or photo album for anniversary
   pictures
Take a portrait of the couple or give gift certificate to a photography studio.

Frame wedding invitation or announcement.
Restore wedding picture.
Painting or photograph of their house, church where they married, or other
   sentimental spot.
Family history—genealogy charts, written or taped experiences.
Visit them and take flowers or a potted plant, candy, their favorite wine, basket
   of fruit, jellies or cheeses, or a book.

Record or tape of favorite kind of music
Give an open house.
Guest book, if they have a party
Bake a wedding cake. Just a white cake with white icing, topped with a plastic
    bride and groom from the variety store, will suffice if you aren't a cake
    decorator.
Arrange a conference call with all the children.
Restage the honeymoon as nearly as possible (same place, same menu, etc.)
Write your local mayor or governor (no more than 4 weeks in advance) re-
    questing that an anniversary greeting be sent the couple. For a greeting
    from the President, write 4 weeks in advance to Greetings Office, The
    White House, Washington, D.C. 20500. He will send greetings for 50th or
    subsequent wedding anniversaries. Include recipient's full names, address,
    Zip code and month, day and year of marriage.
Memory box or shadow box filled with memorabilia
Cake knife
Two silver, crystal, marble or pewter goblets
Silver or handmade bookmarks
Matching reclining chairs
Dinner at a nice restaurant
Tickets to special program or event they enjoy
Double bed lamp with separate dimmer switches
Bulbs, shrub, tree, or rose bush for their yard or give to local park or church
    in their names.
Give altar flowers for their church in their names.
Original artwork—stained glass, painting, sculpture, etc.

Antique Collector

If possible, find out the period, style and kind of antiques preferred by your
friend. Does she or he like seventeenth-century European or early Texas or colonial
American items? Or collect a particular item such as thimbles, candlesticks, or
dolls?

Book on restoration, identification, or pricing of antiques, i.e. *Kovel's An-
    tiques Price List,* Ralph and Terry Kovel (Crown Pub., 1981). A new
    edition is issued every year.

Registry book
Take pictures for insurance or pay for an appraisal.
Shelves or display rack, shadow box for display
Tickets to antique show
Pass down a family heirloom with a written history of the
    item and anecdotes or data about the owners.
Decorative items of the period to complement furniture
    (vase, napkin rings, candlesticks, bookends)

Crochet a dresser scarf, cross-stitch a sampler, paint a tole painting, or make some other craft from her favorite period.

If your friend has another hobby also, find an antique used in that hobby (such as an old book for an avid reader, an antique thimble for a seamstress, old tools for a handyman, old kitchen utensils for a cook, etc.).

Wooden tray, stemware, dishes, pitcher

Jewelry

Restore a picture of the family, old homestead, hometown long ago.

Artist

Art is as diverse a category as clothing. There are too many styles and kinds to list them all. For a gift to be useful, know your friend's medium (oils, watercolor, pen and ink, etc.). For gift ideas in other art forms, see *Crafts.*

Catalogs for artists are listed under *Craft Supplies.*

Tickets to a gallery show

Gift certificate to art supply house, craft catalog, or picture framing shop

Art lessons in person's field

Books on technique, design, favorite medium, favorite artist

Studio apron

Staple gun

100% rag tracing paper

Canvas, canvas portfolio, tote bag

Sketch pad or board for person's medium, e.g.
pen and ink, charcoal, watercolor, etc.

Easel

Mat cutter (used in mounting pictures)

Top quality brushes

Brush holder

Desk top organizer

Art bin box for carrying supplies

Drawing pencils, pastel kit, charcoal pencils, eraser

Collection of paints artist uses—water-based acrylic, watercolor, oils, etc.

Adjustable mannequin

Stool for studio or folding stool for outdoors

Collection of frames, stretcher strips

Palette, palette pad, palette knife (for oil, acrylic, or china painting), paint tray

China painting—pieces of white china or jewelry to paint, sable brushes, liners, pointers, oil paints, china paints, airtight flat storage containers to put mixed paints in to freeze and reuse, decals, adjustable magnifier on stand

Pen and ink—refillable drawing pen, bristol board or paper, India ink, pen points

Bachelor

When I asked people what a bachelor would want, they usually replied, "Mirrored ceiling tiles" or something on that order. But when I asked bachelors about a favorite gift, I got a totally different response, as you see below. See also *Gift Ideas: Adult (Basic), Men, Cook, Fireplace, Host-Hostess, Housewarming,* and hobby categories.

Barbecue grill, hibachi
Picnic basket, ice chest, Thermos®
Box of cheese, sausage, jellies, relishes; basket of fruit; ham, turkey
Membership in health spa, dinner club, YMCA
Two tickets to sporting event, symphony, play, etc.
Passes to movie, bowling alley, miniature golf, etc.
Gift certificate to nice restaurant
Have him over for home-cooked meal.
Frozen, home-cooked meals in one-serving size
Homemade bread, cake, cookies, casserole, etc.—Let him keep the dish.
Coupons for mending, cooking
Maid service
Magazine subscription (see *Magazines: Men,* or special interest area in magazine section)
Book on money or time management, adult development
Money
Gift certificate to clothing store, cleaners
Anything with college or favorite team emblem on it—mug, T-shirt, glasses, cap, etc.
Lessons in disco or ballroom dancing
Tuition for course in woodworking, painting, photography, scuba diving, bridge, etc.
Frame a picture.

More Personal Items
Soap on a rope, cologne, after-shave lotion
Anything handmade—afghan, throw pillow, wall hanging, shirt, picture, bookends, stained glass ornament, whatever you do best
Jewelry—neck chain, bracelet, medallion
Key ring
Cigarette lighter—or Stop Smoking kit or course!
Write him a poem or song.
Bath sheet, giant size towel or towel that fastens around waist
Humorous T-shirt
Personalized license plates, bumper sticker
Heating pad, thermometer, ice pack

Things For The House
Extra loud alarm clock
One cup drip coffee maker, popcorn popper, ice cream freezer, burger cooker

Nice set of glasses or dishes or flatware
Coasters
Serving dishes
Cookbook
Microwave oven
Bar tools (see *Gift Ideas: Bar Gifts*)
Wine rack, wine, liquor
Bed, bath, kitchen, or table linens
Variety pack of paper napkins, coasters, plates for
    entertaining
No-iron cloth napkins
Laundry basket with detergent, stain spray, roll of
    quarters
Book of household hints (stain removal, etc.)
Address book
Calendar with notations of family or other birthdays, an-
    niversaries, etc.
The Greatest Gift Guide Ever
Portable TV, radio, CB
TV trays, card table, folding chairs
Iron, ironing board
Sewing kit
Plants, hanging basket, terrarium
Plaque, painting, poster, needlework picture for the wall
Holiday ornaments or decorations—handmade, if possible

WINE COOLER

Backpacker

A backpacker does not want to be weighed down with unnecessary gear, yet he needs to be prepared for the unexpected. Therefore many of the items below are light-weight versions of useful outdoor gear. Consider whether your backpacker favors winter or summer hiking before selecting seasonal gear. Other ideas will be under *Gift Ideas: Outdoors.*

Catalogs are listed under *Outdoors, Sports.*

Clothing

Identification necklace or bracelet, with medical alert information if applicable
Nylon jacket, poncho, parka, down vest
Wool shirt, chamois shirt
Turtleneck sweater
Sock liners, wool or thermal socks
Wool pants
Stocking cap, sock cap, down hood
Insoles for shoes, shoe laces

Rain gear
Hiking boots; boot wax, sealer, conditioner
Snow shoes, snow goggles
Bandannas

Cooking Gear
Metal match, waterproof matches, plastic match box
Backpacker's grill
Pack stove, fuel bottle or pump
Nesting camp cook set
Pot gripper, long oven mitt
Collapsible water jug
G.I. can opener
Water purifier
Fold-up camp bucket
Dried food (see *Catalogs: Food, Dried*)
Quick-energy or non-perishable foods—beef jerky, peanut butter, nuts

Emergency Equipment
Small first aid kit, first aid book
Compass
Whistle—especially for children
Aerial flare, signal mirror
Instant ice cold compress
Walkie-talkie
Space, emergency or reflector blanket

Other Ideas
Gift certificate to outdoor catalog or store

Pack, pack frame, shoulder bag, stuff bag, rucksack, all kinds of "soft luggage"
Sleeping Bag
Tent
Air pillow
Blanket
Hammock
Light plastic sheet, ground cloth
30 ft. of light, strong, nylon rope; braided utility cord
Camera, camera strap, camera harness, close-up lens, filters, film
Binoculars
Pocket knife, sheath knife, Swiss Army Knife
Small mill file, sharpening stone, honing oil
Folding saw, hatchet, ice ax

Folding scissors
Repair tape for all fabrics
Small sewing kit
Compact waterproof flashlight
Crushproof eyeglass caddy
Plastic tube (map keeper)
Break-down fishing rod
Alarm clock
Pocket calendar
Outdoor, backpacking magazine (see *Magazines: Outdoors*)
Book on packing tours in particular part of country, birds, snakes, wild-
flowers, trees, stars
Books such as
   Backpacking, Lee Schreiber (Stein and Day, 1978).
   Backpacking Equipment, William Kemsley Jr. (Macmillan, 1975).
   Backpacking with Babies and Small Children, Goldie Silverman (Signpost
      Publications, 1975).
   The New Complete Walker, Colin Fletcher (Alfred A. Knopf, 1978).
   Walking in the Wild: Complete Guide to Hiking & Backpacking, Robert
      J. Kelsey (Funk and Wagnalls, 1973).

Bar Gifts

Glasses—cocktail, champagne, cordials, martini, wine, highball, old fash-
ioned, whiskey sour, brandy snifter, mint julep
Decanter
Wine or liquor bottle labels
Wine, liquor
Wine rack
Wine cooler
Cocktail napkins, picks, stir and dip
   straws, paper party napkins
Bottle and can opener, corkscrew,
   waiter's corkscrew with wire cutter
Cocktail strainer
Lime squeezer
Pourer, siphon
Jigger—silver, crystal, with college logo
Muddler spoon, jigger spoon, bar spoon
Ice bucket, ice tongs
Ice crusher
Bar towel
Bar light

Bar Mitzvah or Bat Mitzvah

These are ceremonies for Jewish 13-year-olds celebrating reaching the age of religious responsibility. The bat mitzvah for girls is relatively new. See also *Gift Ideas: 11- to 14-Year-Olds.*

Religious jewelry—Star of David, mezuzah, menorah, chai

Prayer book, Torah, Holy Scriptures (Chumash)
Biography of Jewish hero, heroine
Stories or poems or music by Jewish author, composer
Savings bond; add to savings account
Clock radio, cassette recorder, camera, watch
Kiddush cup (boy)
Shabbet candlestick (girl)
Subscription to Jewish magazine
Israeli art object, jewelry, or coin made into medallion
Donation to a charity in the child's name

Plant a tree in Israel in the child's name. Contact the Jewish National Fund, 42 E. 69th St., New York, NY 10021 or the local office. Trees are $5 each.

Boater

Canoeists and sailors do not like to claim kin, but they do share part of the same general gift list below. The items under Big Boats were gathered for people who have sleeping and eating facilities on their boats. Many boat owners are particular about brands and basic boat gear and instruments. If you do try to buy a part for the boat, be sure to have the model and serial number of the engine. See also *Gift Ideas: Fisherman, Water Skier,* and *Outdoors.*

Catalog sources are listed under *Catalogs: Boater*

Basic

Books on boating, fishing, marine life, maritime history, sea tales
Course on water safety, racing, technique
Model of his type of boat with name of boat on it
Desk or household items with nautical motif
Subscription to boating magazine (see *Magazines: Boating*)
Life vests (for pet, too!)
Flares, air horn, emergency whistle, distress flag
First aid kit
Fishing rod holder
Weather radio
Canoe chair
Picnic basket, ice chest with flotation in sides, Thermos®
Collapsible water jug

Insulated drink holders
Floating knife
Floating key chain
Floating flashlight
Binoculars
Compass
Chart book of maps for favorite river
Nylon poncho, jacket, pants
Swim suit or cover-up, sun hat, thongs, beach towel
Nylon tote bags, pouches, cushion with zippered pockets, ditty bag
Trailer lock
Boat cover
Outboard motor lock, case of motor oil, motor cover, motor weed guard
Dry land test flush (to clean motor)
Battery charger
Boat light
Marine engine tune-up kit

Big Boats

T-shirt with name of boat, or reading "Captain" or "Crew"
Nautical charts from Defense Mapping Agency, US Naval Observatory, Bldg. 56, Washington, D.C. 20305.
Tie with nautical motif
Deck shoes, sandals, rubber boots
Foul weather gear
Sailing gloves, all-weather gloves
Sailing cap
Nautical napkins with name of boat
Non-slip unbreakable dishware, nautical dishware and mugs
Small refrigerator
Boat barbecue grill
Seafood or galley cookbook
Portable fan
Cabin dehumidifier to prevent mildew
Yacht bell
Log book
Cabin magazine rack, lights
Folding table, chairs; deck chair
Beach chair
Portable toilet
Boarding ladder
Novelty pennants, flags, e.g. ball and chain (wife aboard); flag staff
Ship's clock, chronometer, barometer
Piloting aids—sextant, speed-time-distance computer, range finder
Gauges—thermometer, wind chill, rain gauge, wind indicator
Chart case, chart holder, chart weight

Illuminated magnifier
Spotting scope
Sailing timer
Nautical almanac
Tools for boat—adjustable end wrench, slip joint pliers, pipe wrench, vise grip,
    several sizes of screwdrivers, box end wrench set, hammer, plug wrench,
    etc.; toolbox
Box of spare parts—distributor points, condenser, coil, spark plugs, fuel pump,
    fuel filter (for diesel engine)
Rigging knife
Boat burglar alarm
Fog horn
Floating rescue light
Fire extinguisher, smoke detector
Safety netting to protect area between railing and deck
Inflatable boat, life raft
Dock edging
Sail repair kit, yachtman's sewing kit
Magnetic playing cards
Insulated boat blanket
Spillproof, windproof ashtray
Screw-in, metal cup holders that swivel

Bowler

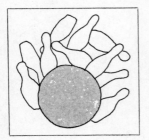

Bowling ball without holes—must be drilled to
    fit fingers
Bowling bag
Bowling shoes
Bowling towel
Bowling ball polisher, buffer
Bowling glove, wrist support
Passes to bowling alley
Books, subscription to magazine on bowling (see
    Magazines: Sports)
Anything with bowling motif—T-shirt, mug,
    plaque, figurine, key chain, pillow
Comedy bowling ball (brick with 2 or 3 holes)

Bridesmaid

Jewelry—stick pin, necklace, bracelet, earrings, neck chain, pendant, locket
Jewelry box, ring box, crystal ring holder
Perfume
Bud vase, china flowers
Stained glass window or table ornament

Small picture frame, photograph album, photo collage frame
Photograph of wedding party, photograph album
Personalized note paper
Silver or crystal candy, relish or compote dish
Silver or crystal jigger
Serving tray, serving bowl, Revere bowl
Silverplate, pewter, wood, or brass trivet
Set of crystal coasters
Wood or crystal and silver salt and pepper shakers
Monogrammed linen roll cover or hand towel
Any item made by bride—pottery bowl; needlepoint bookmark or key ring; embroidered pillowcases; small decoupaged, painted, or cross-stitched picture; macramé plant hanger; etc.

Camper

See *Gift Ideas: Outdoors* for more ideas.
Catalogs with camping equipment are listed under *Outdoors, Sports.*

Golden Eagle or Golden Age Passport to national parks (see *Gift Ideas: Traveler* for details)
Books on camping with children, equipment, campsites, first aid, birds, wildflowers, trees, wild animals of the area, star gazing
Rand McNally Campgrounds and Trailer Park Guide, 1982.
Wheelers, RV Resort & Campground Guide, Print Media Services, 1982.
Magazine subscription (see *Magazines: Outdoors*)
Humorous laundry bag (drawstring)
Elastic or nylon clothes line
Portable toilet
Portable or catalytic heater
Small fan—battery-operated or electric
Heavy-duty extension cord
Steel mirror
Baby carrying devices—sling, cradleboard, backpack carrier
Thermal, insulated, or fishnet underwear
Cold weather clothes, parka, outdoor clothing
Personalized name tags to sew or iron into youngsters' clothes
Matching flannel shirts, nightshirts
Film
Weather radio
Automobile roof rack with cover
Fly swatter
Spray for ants or flying insects

Basic Gear
Sleeping bag, ground cloth, inflatable pillow, air mattress, foam pad, cot
Foot pump or 12-volt air compressor for blowing up air mattresses
Tent, screened room; tent bag, tent frame bag

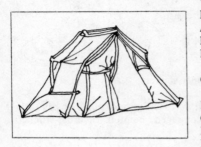

Waterproof flashlight
Lantern—light-weight and reliable
Ax, hatchet, folding saw, shovel
Folding chairs, stool, table
Folding canvas water bucket, collapsible water jug, canteen
Canvas or nylon duffel bag, stuff sacks, soft luggage
Binoculars
Good sunglasses
Pocket knife
Plastic bottles, soap holder, toothbrush holder

Safety Equipment
Small first aid kit and book
Insect repellant, sting stopper
Compass
Whistle for everyone
Fire extinguisher
Signal mirror
Emergency or reflective blanket

Cooking Gear
Camp toaster
Portable stove, reflector stove, and appropriate fuel
Collapsible oven
Charcoal, waterproof matches
Picnic basket
Dried food (see *Catalogs: Food, Dried*)
Grocery staples—instant hot drinks, soup, cereals, peanut butter, non-perishables
Nesting cookware
Unbreakable plastic or metal dishes, mugs
Dutch oven—cast iron or thick aluminum
Oversized frying pan or griddle—cast iron or aluminum
Insulated ice chest, Thermos®
Long oven mitt
Long-handled fork, tongs, spatula, spoon
Outdoor cookbook such as *Roughing It Easy,* Dian Thomas (Warner Books)
Picnic tablecloth or blanket (washable, please!)
Tablecloth clamps

Christmas Specials

Tickets to "The Nutcracker" or other special
   holiday entertainment
Decoupage an appropriate Christmas card on
   plaque or mount on ⅛" plywood.

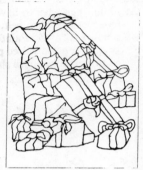

Holiday wall hanging, decoupage picture, bell
   pull, hand towel, apron, vest, tie
Door or doorknob decorations
Wreath—greenery, pine cones, nuts, candy,
   sweetgum balls, braided fabric (see *Things to
   Make*), straw, bread dough
Centerpiece—with candles, greenery, mini-tree,
   basket of small pine cones with red bows,
   shiny Christmas balls
Mints, cookies in holiday shapes
Fruitcake and bread
Jellies, pickles, relishes
Fancy plate or dish filled with homemade goodies
Plate of shaped cookies (include the cookie cutter!)
Brandy snifter full of candy and decorated like face of Santa Claus
Advent calendar (wall or door hanging with 25 spaces for the first 25 days of
   December). Make in shape of Christmas tree (use felt, fabric, or paint on
   posterboard) or in shape of calendar or plaque. Add small toy, ornament,
   candy cane, decoration to one space each day.
Tree skirt—quilted fabric, stitchery, patchwork, felt
Stockings for adults
Make your own Christmas cards—an original block print, poem, drawing,
   puzzle, carol; card with family photograph.
Christmas music—records, tapes, concert tickets, song books, sheet music
Books on Christmas—decorations, customs, stories, art, carols
The Christmas Lover's Handbook, Lasley Gober (Betterway, 1985)
Card holder—basket lined with bright fabric
Nativity scenes—fabric, ceramic, wood, one for the children to play with
Prepare a family or neighborhood Christmas pageant.
Go caroling at a nursing home or home of shut-in or special friend.
Small tree for child to decorate for his own room

Ornaments

Kits to make—wooden, felt, sequined, stuffed
Crocheted, knitted, needlepoint
Dough ornaments (see *Things to Make*)
Cookie cutters tied with gingham or red ribbon
Wooden (natural finish or painted)—Trace cookie cutters onto ⅛" plywood
   and cut out shapes with jigsaw.
Heirloom—crystal, etched glass, gold-plated, silver, Gorham, Hallmark

Christmas Stocking Stuffers & Hanukkah Gifts

Children

Any small toy or game—see children's age categories

Anything they have to **have, but in a** fancy style—underwear, socks, barrettes, hair ribbons, **belt, shoe laces,** comb, brush, mirror (Decorate or personalize with Wet Paint™.)

Decorative or personalized **pens or pencils,** erasers, crayons, chalk, notepads, coloring book, **pencil sharpener,** ruler, scissors

Candy, gum, fruit

Decorated toothbrush; soap sculpture

Bubble bath, shampoo in cute containers

Balloons, jacks, jump rope, marbles, playing cards

Jewelry

Bookmark, small book

Cassette tape

Packet of coins, currency or collectibles (stamps, baseball cards, stickers, etc.)

Card announcing a magazine subscription (see *Magazines: Children*)

Personalized Christmas ornament

Adult

Notecards, pretty postcards, stamps

Pens, pencils, notepads

Wallet-sized photos

Gift certificate

Card announcing a magazine subscription

Bookmark, small book

Smoking cure

Film

Decorative candle

Key chain or key ring

Jewelry

Comb, compact, lipstick, nail polish

Scented or initialed soap

Small size shampoo, hand lotion, cologne, perfume, after-shave lotion

Hose, gloves, socks, scarves, belt, folding umbrella

Handkerchiefs, purse-size tissue

Candy, gum, fruit, nuts, favorite canned food (oysters, bean dip), homemade jelly or relish, bottle of wine

Kitchen utensils, cookie cutters, magnetic memo holders

Small tools for hobby

Golf tees or balls, tennis balls; gun shells; fishing tackles, flies, worms

Flower bulbs, seed packets
Fireplace matches, decorative book matches, cigarette lighter
Thermometers—cooking, indoor-outdoor
Rechargeable batteries
Pocket-sized flashlight
Pocket calculator
Christmas ornament
Any small gift from other gift categories

Clergy

Clergy of course are not a separate species. Like the rest of us, they enjoy a variety of hobbies and interests. The wife of one Presbyterian minister saved for weeks to give her husband *The Interpreter's Bible* for their 25th wedding anniversary. What did he give her? A lacy black negligee! Some occasions, however, do call for a gift relating to a clergyman's profession. Here are some ideas especially appropriate for members of the clergy.

Business cards (with church's name on them, too)
Medallion or other religious jewelry
Stole in liturgical color or hand-embroidered
Personalized copy of denominational hymn book
Antique Bibles or denominational books
Religious reference book, e.g. *The Interpreter's One Volume Commentary on the Bible,* Charles M. Layman, ed. (Abingdon Press, 1971).
The Layman's Parallel Bible, (Zondervan, 1973).
Mementos from the Holy Land, Vatican, or other place of special religious significance for the person
Christmas decoration or tree ornament
Gift certificate to book store, other favorite store
Subscription to weekly news or special interest magazine
Tickets for family to play, symphony, ball game, etc.
Homemade goodies; gift pack of cheese, sausage, jellies; basket of fruit
Any handicraft by you
Give book, tree, shrub, hymnals, or equipment or furnishings to the church in his name.

For Office

Plaque, picture, figurine, stitchery meaningful to him (serious or humorous)
Desk picture frame
Desk organizers
Have diploma or certificates matted or framed.
Personalized memo pads, pencils
See *Gift Ideas: Desk Dwellers*

Collector

This list could be as endless as the list of things people collect—matchbooks, beer cans, thimbles, plates, dolls, antique cameras, pictures of roadrunners, and on and on. Here are specific ideas for collectors of two common items—coins and stamps—and general ideas appropriate for collectors of diverse items. Also see *Gift Ideas: Antique Collector.*

Catalogs specializing in collectibles are listed under *Collectors.*

General

Magazine subscription (see *Magazines: Collectors*)

Gift certificate to shop or catalog that carries what he/she collects

Book on identifying silver hallmarks, cut-glass signatures, or other special markings

Book on the appropriate collectible—its history, how-to, antique or rare items, museum collections, price lists

A piece for the collection; antique or foreign item

Display shelves, plate holder, stand

Line a shadow box with velvet for displaying small items.

Album for postcards, stamps, matchbooks, etc.

Registry—book for listing items in collection with place for purchase, insurance, and appraisal information

Take pictures of collection for insurance.

Doll house furniture, accessories—Be sure item is same scale as doll house (most are scaled 1 inch to 1 foot) and in correct era (Victorian, Early American, etc.)

Stamp Collector

Stamp album, stock books, first day cover album

Stamp tongs, hinges, acetate or glassine envelopes, magnifying glass, perforation gauge, color gauge

Watermark detector fluid, tray

Stamp map, atlas, globe

Save commemorative stamps off your mail and include undamaged ones with a card.

From post office, "theme" packets of stamps, mint stamps, first day covers

Stamp press

Stamp lift (for removing old hinges)

New stamps from any foreign country you visit

Coin Collector

Coin mounts, holders, tubes; stock book, album; acetate envelopes
Magnifying glass
Coin preservative
Silver dollars, mint coin
Proof set of new year coins—Write Bureau of the Mint, 55 Mint St., San
   Francisco, Cal. 94175 for ordering information.
Guide Book of United States Coins, R.S. Yeoman (Western Publishing Co.).
   New edition every summer.

College Graduation

See also *Gift Ideas: Men, Women, Adult (Basic), Bachelor, Single Woman,*
and other special interest categories.

Rabbit's foot
Frame the diploma.
Class ring
Mug, plaque, T-shirt, anything with school's
   logo
Membership in alumni or professional
   association
Car or special trip
Gift certificate to medical, architectural, dental,
   or other professional supply house

Reference book or tools in graduate's field
Portrait of the graduate
Watch, jewelry
Pocket calculator, radio
Camera
Photograph album
Typewriter
Sewing machine
Items for setting up housekeeping—see *Gift Ideas: Cook, Host-Hostess,* or
   Housewarming.
Cash or wallet (with cash inside!)
Book on investment, money management, e.g. *Sylvia Porter's New Money
   Book for the 80's,* Sylvia Field Porter (Avon, 1980) or *The Only Investment
   Guide You'll Ever Need,* Andrew Tobias (Harcourt Brace Jovanovich or
   Bantam Books, 1978) or *Money Dynamics for the 1980's,* Venita Van
   Caspel (Prentice Hall, 1980).
Book on time management
Book on adult development, e.g. *Passages: Predictable Crises of Adult Life,*
   Gail Sheehy (E.P. Dutton & Co., 1974).
Bookends
Pen and pencil set

College Student Away from Home

Dormitory life is a unique experience and students living in dorms have unique needs. Other gift ideas are listed under *Bachelor, Single Woman, Adult (Basic), Women, Men* and special interest categories.

For students living in apartments, see *Gift Ideas: Host-Hostess, Cook,* or *Housewarming.*

Money

Lots of mail

Telephone calls from home, visits from home-town folks

Telephone credit card, pay for private telephone; coupons for long distance telephone calls or gift certificate from telephone company

Tickets for transportation home

Subscription to hometown newspaper

Magazine subscription (maybe in his field of study)

Take student out to eat.

Passes to movie, bowling alley, fast food restaurant

Gift certificate to a nice restaurant

"Care package" of non-perishable food—beef jerky, sunflower seeds, fruit rolls, dried fruit, canned fruit, crackers, peanut butter, honey, nuts, raisins, coffee, tea

Cookie jar (full of homemade cookies)

Homemade goodies—cake, candy, cookies; or fresh fruit

Heating element for coffee, soup

Small coffee pot, mugs (personalized)

Popcorn popper

Small insulated ice chest

Typewriter

Desk lamp

Stationery (addressed and stamped?), roll of stamps, stamped postcards

Portable bookcase, small chest of drawers

Bookends, bookplates, bookmark

Address book

Pencil sharpener, pencil holder, transparent tape, scissors, stapler

Bag of ball point pens, pencils (personalized)

Photo album, scrapbook, camera, film

Cassette tape recorder-player

Clock radio, portable radio, small TV, alarm clock (loud!)

Luggage, tote bags, heavy duty clothes bag (for travel)

Drip-dry, no-care clothing

Cute laundry bag or clothes basket with roll of quarters

Personalized labels for clothes, linens

Clothes drying rack, elastic clothesline

Iron, ironing board
Bed and bath linens, blanket, throw pillows
Wall posters
Basic sewing kit
Mop, broom, cleansing powder
Personal care appliance (see *Appendix: Small Electric Appliances*)
Potted plant
Coin bank—for drink machines, pay phones, etc.
Official Preppy Handbook, Lisa Birnbach (Workman Publishing Co., 1980)
What Color Is Your Parachute?, Richard N. Bolles (Ten Speed Press, 1981)

Cook

Gourmet cooks prefer copper cookware, wooden utensils, and French names for their dishes. Cooks not into gourmet foods usually appreciate something that makes food easier to prepare or prettier to serve. Outdoor cooks need special equipment. See *Appendix: Small Electric Appliances—Food Preparation and Serving Aids* and *Gift Ideas: Host-Hostess.*

Catalogs: Food and *Housewares* offer a variety of equipment and other appropriate gift items.

Any Cook

Kitchen clock, kitchen timer
Food processing machine, accessories
Herb garden in pretty pots or planter, sprouting kit

Absorbent kitchen towels; oven mitts
Apron—patchwork, holiday, pinafore style
Baking dish, skillet, or cake pan full of casserole, cookies, etc. Let cook keep the dish.
Cookbooks of all kinds: quick meals, freeze-ahead meals, foreign fare, favorite organization's cookbook, microwave cooking, e.g. *Mastering Microwave Cooking,* Maria Luisa and Jack Denton Scott (Bantam Books, 1976) or *General Electric Microwave Guide and Cookbook* (Random House, 1978).
Cookbook holder (Lucite)
Recipe holder, recipe box, decorative recipe cards, plastic sleeves for recipe cards
Measuring cups, spoons; spatula, sifter (electric kind is available), whip, tongs, pastry brush, baster
Mixing bowls—Covered ones are useful.
Spoon rest
Cutting board (wood, ceramic or Lucite)
Thermometers—meat and poultry, candy, oven, refrigerator
Freezer-to-oven cookware, non-stick cookware

Cookware—double boiler, roasting pan, baking pan (with cover), bread pan, muffin tin, cake or pie pan, skillet

Canister set—airtight

Cooling racks

Food scale

Jar opener

Knives—French chef, bread, butcher, roast slicer, boner, utility, paring, frozen food, steak set

Knife holder, knife block

Sharpening steel or ceramic hone

Pastry cloth, rolling pin cover, pastry board, bread baking stone

Spice rack

Microwave pans—browning tray, muffin pan, cake pan, bacon rack, casserole or baking pans

Pizza pan, pizza paddle, pizza brick

Omelet pan

Fondue pot

Wok set

Butter warmer, butter molds

Pressure cooker

Sausage maker kit

Salad spinner

Meat grinder, coffee grinder

Vegetable steamer

Roaster

Food chopper

Cheese grater (hand held at table), cheese slicer

Sprimp cleaner and sheller, crab shears

Pea shelling attachment for mixer

Meat tenderizer

Garlic press, radish press, melon baller, meat ball press, tomato corer, apple corer, pineapple cutter, peeling machine

Pot racks—wrought iron, copper, brass

Three-tier hanging basket for fresh vegetables, fruit

Sieves, spatter top, pot drainer, double-boiler maker

Kitchen shears, poultry shears

Shish kabob skewers

Airtight plastic storage containers

Canning equipment—jars, lids, labels

Cake decorating kit, book, equipment

Shaped cake pans, cookie cutters, candy molds

Salad molds

Cake carrier, pie carrier

Wheeled chopping block

Bread box

Pretty serving dishes (see *Gift Ideas: Host-Hostess*)

Door or wall rack to expand pantry space

Gourmet Cook

Subscription (See *Magazines: Cooking*)
Cheese or wine tasting course
Tuition for gourmet cooking class
Dinner at gourmet restaurant
The Cooks' Catalog, edited by James Beard, Milton Glaser, Burton Wolf, Barbara Poses Kafka, Helen S. Witty & Association of the Good Cooking School, (Harper & Row, 1975). Comparison test results of over 4,000 items, kitchen utensils, appliances, machines, tools, knives.
Hard-to-find seasonings, foreign food items (see *Catalogs: Food*) or gourmet foods such as pheasant, caviar, pâté, lobster tails, shad roe, sardines
Wine label album
Asparagus or artichoke steam rack
Canapé maker, lobster scissors, steak hammer
Garlic storage jar
Marble rolling pin and pastry board
Soufflé dish, pâté en croûte dish
Quiche pans—ceramic, glass, stainless steel
Au gratin dishes
Wooden utensils, chop sticks (disposable or decorative), whisk, whip
Clay bread pans, roasting pot
Bakers' black steel baking, bread pans
Cast iron or copper cookware
Carbon steel or stainless cutlery, food slicer
Double boiler
Pasta maker, tortilla press

Outdoor Cook

Make napkins out of colorful terry cloth or Permapress® cotton.
Barbecue grill, hibachi, portable grill
Charcoal, fire starter, long matches, electric charcoal lighter
Grill cleaning brush
Grill attachments—second layer, rib rack, broiler basket, corn and potato grill, tray
Long-handled tools—tongs, fork, spatula, baster, knife, spoon
Oven mitt
Outdoor cookbook
Electric rotisserie
Shish kabob skewers
Box of decorative paper plates, napkins, cups
Wicker paper plate holders
Plastic dishware; insulated glasses, mugs, serving dishes
Steak serving plates
Picnic table, tablecloth, tablecloth clamps
Lawn furniture, folding chairs
Chef's apron
Mesh or net food cover

Crafts

Choose a gift from a variety of popular craft areas—either your friend's favorite craft or give her a complete kit (with all supplies included) in a new area so she can see if she likes it. See also *Gift Ideas: Needleworker, Seamstress,* or *Artist* and *Catalogs: Craft Supplies.*

For Any Craftsperson

Gift certificate to craft store or catalog

Subscription to craft magazine

Books on the craft—techniques, variations, famous collections

Kits for the crafts listed below or for papier mâché, decoupage, tole painting, plastic molding, string art, weaving, wire art, basketry, pom-pom craft, plaster casting, shrink art, woodcarving, sequin or felt crafts, paint-by-number, mosaics, model building, metal enameling, clear casting

Sharing Barbara's Mail, Box 10423, Springfield, Mo. 65808. $12 for 6 issues. Bi-monthly newsletter on craft networking, pricing, legal matters, marketing, etc.

Catalog Sources for Creative People, Margaret Boyd (Box 6232, Augusta, Ga. 30906) $8.95ppd.

Creative Cash: How to Sell Your Crafts, Needlework, Designs & Knowhow, Barbara Brabec (Artisan Crafts, Box 10423, Springfield, Mo. 65808) $8.95ppd.

National Directory of Shops/Galleries, Shows/Fairs, Chris Weills (Box 4520, Berkeley, Cal. 94704) $14.45ppd. For those wanting to sell or place their wares on commission.

A finished piece in her favorite area such as a pom-pom refrigerator note holder, pottery pitcher, hand-painted wooden Christmas ornament, hand-woven shawl, etc.

Lessons in a new or favorite craft area

Shelves, display rack or box for displaying finished work

Batik

Bamboo brushes, alcohol lamp, stretcher frame, white silk or cotton material, dyes, tjanting needle for outlining

Candlemaking

Coloring wax (or a box of old Crayola stubs), candle thermometer, molds, candle holders, candle scents

Ceramics

Greenware, glazes, molds, slip, cleaning tools, pattern cutting tools, decals for decoration

Enameling
Metal kiln, enameling rack, swirling tool, tweezers, enameling spatula, copper shapes

Jewelry Making
Book on identifying stones and minerals, field guide to gem and mineral localities

Anvil, bench pin, jeweler's saw, pin or bench vise, tin snips, metal shears, cutting broach, dapping punches, cutters, blocks to shape and cut metal and wax, pivot and twist drills, hand drill, hammer mallet, wire cutter, mandrel, pliers, metal stamp

Polishing, buffing kit; buffing cloth; burnisher; emery paper, files

Magnifying glass or loupe

Ring stick or measuring gauge

Metal scales, metal test kit

Soldering gun, accessories; electric engraver

Jeweler's work bench

Jeweler's casting machine

Miniature power tool kit; accessories for polishing, cutting, sanding

Rock tumbler, polisher

Polished gemstones

Mountings for gems (stick pin, pendant, brooch, earring, ring, belt buckle)

Velvet lined boxes for finished work

Leathercraft
Package of scrap leather

Anvil, mallet, tooling kit, stamping kit

Leather stripper

Leather shears, sewing awl, lacing needle, snap button fastener, edge bevelers, hole punch set, leather point machine needles, X-Acto knife

Belt buckle

Macrame
Macramé board, cord or jute, rings, beads

Potter
Potter's wheel; rolling pin, knives, scrapers, sponges, plastic dishpan and waste cans for storage or clean up; good brushes; tools for trimming, decorating, carving; glazes, stains (lead-free, if possible); 25 to 100 pounds of clay (many types and colors); rolling boards; kiln; balance scales to weigh glaze chemicals; any handmade pottery piece; pottery lifter

Sculpting
Modeling stand to hold pieces while working; armatures, mannekin; carving tools, knives, rasps; modeling wheel

Stained Glass
Pattern books, lead, soldering iron, glass or circle cutter, glass pliers, glass handler's gloves, soldering tool stand, belt sander, "L" square

Cyclist

The degree of dedication to cycling will determine how appropriate some of these items are for the person you have in mind. There are several kinds of cyclists—neighborhood biker, motocross fan, racer, and touring cyclist. Some of these suggestions overlap categories.

See also *Catalogs: Cycling.*

Neighborhood Biker, General

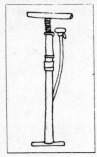

Tire pump
Personalized license tag
Child seat with foot guard for parent's bike
Reflectors, reflective clothing, ankle bands, pedals
Padded seat for adults
Horn
Bicycle lock and cable
Speedometer, odometer
Carrier rack, basket
New bicycle
Subscription (See *Magazines: Cycling*)
Bicycle rack for car

Motocross

Pads for frame, cross bar, stem
Grips for handlebars
Number plates

Racer

(They don't really want accessories because of the excess weight.)
Cycling shorts made of wool, polyester or helenca with chamois seat
Jerseys with some wool
Toe clips and straps
Cycling cap, protective helmet

Tourist

Guide book on bike paths in his area
Lighting set
Wool leg, arm, foot warmers
Nylon, zippered jacket with hood
Rain poncho made for cyclists so loose ends won't catch in spokes
Fingerless gloves with padded palm and mesh back
Clips for pants to keep them from catching in spokes
Bicycle radio, AM/CB bicycle base transceiver
Panniers, other touring bags, belt pack
Plastic saddle cover (for rainy weather); fanny pads
Bicycle repair tools
Compass
Rearview mirror to clip to glasses

Water bottle that clips to bike
Waterless hand cleaner
Swiss Army Knife—Screwdriver, slicing knife, bottle opener are necessities.
Some useful books:
  American Biking Atlas and Touring Guide, Sue Browder (Workman, 1974.)
  Anybody's Bike Book, Tom Cuthbertson (Ten Speed Press, 1979). Witty
    manual of bicycle repairs.
  DeLong's Guide to Bicycles & Bicycling, Fred DeLong (Chilton Book Co.,
    1978).
  The New Complete Book of Bicycling, Eugene Sloane (Simon & Schuster,
    1974). Comprehensive book on history, physical fitness, racing,
    tourism, maintenance.
  Richard's Bicycle Book, Richard Ballentine (Ballentine Books, 1976).

Organizations

American Youth Hostels, National Campus, Delaplane, Va. 22025.
    Membership allows use of hostels in various parts of U.S. and Europe.
Cyclists' Touring Club, 69 Meadrow, Godalming, Surrey, Eng. GO7 3HS.
    Membership about $15. Bimonthly magazine; directory of accommoda-
    tions, tours.
International Bicycle Touring Society, 2115 Paseo Dorado, La Jolla, Cal.
    92037. Membership, $10 (must be 21 or older). Sponsors 15 tours a year
    in U.S. and Europe.
League of American Wheelmen, Box 988, Baltimore, Md. 21203. Individual
    membership, $18; family, $24. Monthly magazine, bulletins on tours in
    U.S. and abroad.
United States Cycling Federation, 1750 E. Boulder, Colorado Springs, Colo.
    80909. Racing license and membership, $10–25. Controlling organization
    for racing in U.S.

Desk Dweller.

Anyone who spends a lot of time at a desk might enjoy a gift from this list, in-
tended to help secretaries think of gifts for their bosses and vice versa. See other
gift idea categories such as *Just a Little Something, Adult (Basic)* or hobby area.

A raise
Magazine subscription
Gift certificate to major department store
Amagift—album of over 40 gifts to choose from
    in your selected price range from local Am-
    way distributors.
Coffee mug with name on it
Attaché case, portfolio
Name plate for desk
Supply holders—pen or pencil holder, tape
    holder
Drawer or desk organizers

Tissue holder, letter holder—hand-decorated
Paper weight
Unusual pens, pen and pencil set, mechanical pencil
Electric pencil sharpener
Desk calendar or desk diary
Letter opener
Telephone shoulder rest
Small standing picture frame or hanging one if he has a private office
Small clock for desk or wall
Cute note pads or memo pads—or personalized ones
Personal yellow pages
List finder or roto-phone file with removable pages
Wallet-size calculator, calculator stand
Potted plant for desk
Dictionary
Roget's International Thesaurus (Harper & Row, 1979).
The Greatest Gift Guide Ever
Chair cushion
Food box of ham, turkey, cheese, jelly, sausage, etc.

Elderly at Own Home

While many senior citizens have hobbies (look for gift ideas under *Cook, Handyman, Gardener* and other interest categories), they also have needs particular to their age group. Safety devices, expendable items (because many are in small apartments or have all the "accessories" they want), and convenience items are especially welcome. For other gift ideas, see *Handicapped, Nursing Home Residents, Visually Impaired, Hearing Impaired, Adult (Basic), Men* and *Women* categories.

Do a home project—paint a room, clean garage, do yardwork, etc.
Coupon book for shopping, yardwork, rides, etc.
Go Christmas caroling at his/her home; take simple refreshments.
Holiday decoration, Christmas tree or ornaments
Ask mayor, governor, or president to send birthday greetings. Contact
   mayor's or governor's office or see *Anniversaries* for White House address.
Tuition in leisure class—bridge, photography, ceramics, etc.
Tuition for Elderhostel, Suite 200, 100 Boylston, Mass. 02116. Program of
   over 400 colleges and universities around the U.S. and overseas which
   offer low-cost residential, academic study in diverse areas (dreams to
   economics to literature) for persons over 60 and spouses. Maximum fee
   of $180 includes one week's room, board, and tuition (not transportation
   to the city). $10 for year's catalogs.
Membership in American Association of Retired Persons, 215 Long Beach
   Blvd., Long Beach , Cal. 90801. Bimonthly magazine (*Modern Maturity*);
   special rates on insurance, drugs, travel, etc. One year membership, $5.
Arrange conference call with scattered family members.

Tape a family gathering and send them tape.
Cassette recorder or player, tapes (especially religious music, Bible study)
Photo of family, wallet photos, photo wheel or album
Visit on a special day.
Visit on any day and it will be special.
Lots of mail
Have old photographs copied or restored.
Anything made by grandchildren or children
Have grandchildren draw a picture, call, or send a note.
Tickets and transportation to entertainment or sports event, movie, etc.
Dinner at your home or restaurant
Golden Age Passport to national parks (see *Gift Ideas: Traveler*)
Bible, other books or magazines in large print
Books, bookmarks
Magazine subscription
Assorted greeting cards, stationery, stamps
Calendar
Gift certificate to beauty parlor to have hair fixed
Radio or TV
Small electric heater or fan
Snug Sack™, afghan, electric blanket
Telephone amplifier
Gift certificate from telephone company
Energy-saving improvements—sun screen, weather stripping, storm door, etc.
Automatic garage door opener
Bath tub railing
Smoke detector
Deadbolts—Install them, too!
Door viewer
Railing for outdoor steps
Meals for freezer
Box of fruit, candy, cheese, teas, coffees
Small appliance like burger cooker, small coffee pot (see *Appendix: Small Electric Appliances*)
Jar opener; zipper pull
Lighted magnifying glass
Bird feeder or bird bath
Wind chimes
Seeds, potted plant, flower bulbs, terrarium
New linens
Assortment of light bulbs
Sun-catcher for window

Extra Special

A gift from this list will be long remembered.

Membership in professional, historical, scientific, or alumni association
Membership in Young Men's (or Women's) Christian Association, community
center, swim club; local museum, zoo or symphony society
Tuition in a leisure or academic class
Children can make coupon books for parents or special friends for free yard
mowing, weeding, dishwashing, housework, babysitting, etc.
Let a child select a pet from the local animal shelter.
Keep their children overnight or for a few days.
Donate a book in her name to the local, church or school library.
Write a song, poem, or story for the person.
Dedicate a book to him or her.
Create an original painting, stitchery, sculpture, etc.
Have older member of family tell on tape about his childhood, special trip, or
other interesting part of his life. Copy tapes for other family members.
Call or write if you haven't in a long time.
Give a gift in your friend's name to a local charity, church, or school.

Plant a tree at a local park, church, or school with
friend's name on plaque.
Plant a tree in his or her yard.
Quarter of beef for freezer
Loan a gasoline credit card for a trip.
Pay for the whole trip.
Pay for the car.
Pay for the car insurance.
Say, "I love you."
Unusual message services:

Balloon Bouquets—$25 up for arrangements of large
balloons. Can accompany inflatable toys or bot-
tles of spirits. Call toll-free 1-800-424-2323 for office nearest you.

Eastern Onion—Scores of songs to be delivered by phone or in person (with
choice of crazy costumes). $15 up. Consult local telephone directory
for nearby office.

Fortune Cookie Factory—Call 1-415-781-1998 for details on sending a
foot-long fortune cookie ($9 with your own message) or a box of 50
regular-sized cookies ($14.50).

Kron Chocolatier—Chocolates in assorted shapes and sizes. Request a free
brochure from 506 Madison Ave., New York, N.Y. 10022.

Music Box Musical Messages—Have a tuxedoed messenger deliver a
personalized telegram written just for your friend ($40) or send a
telephone-gram ($20). Get more details from 1-800-221-9820 (toll-
free).

Nationwide Gift Liquor—Send a favorite brand of wine, liquor or
champagne at cost plus $10. Order toll-free from 1-800-528-6148.

Singing Telegram of America Referral System—Each agency offers slightly different songs, services and costumes so call toll-free 1-800-323-0678 for the agency nearest you.

TeleCake—Send the cake of your choice across the miles for $22.50 up. Order toll-free from 1-800-453-5710.

TeleWine—Pair a bottle of wine up with roses, cheese or fruit for a minimum $35. Call toll-free 1-800-223-2660.

Wacky Wires and Wonders—Send brownies with buttercream messages written on top. One-pound box is $8 plus handling. Order toll-free from 1-800-453-5710.

Western Union—Singing telegrams by phone or in person. Call your local office for details.

Family

For holiday giving, many people select one gift for the whole family instead of buying presents for each person. This list will provide ideas for years.

Subscription to a magazine like *National Geographic, Smithsonian*

Subscription to magazine about their state—check with state highway department.

Books—encyclopedia, stargazing, bird or wild flower guide, games, art, travel guide, road atlas, regional history

The New Games Book, New Games Foundation (Doubleday, 1976). *More New Games* (Doubleday, 1981). Non-competitive games.

The Greatest Gift Guide Ever

Bookends

Song book

Records, tapes, holders for these

The Ungame (The Ungame Co.), a Christian family game

Playing cards, board games, dominoes, chess, checkers, Chinese checkers, Yahtzee™, Hi Q®, Parcheesi®

Jigsaw puzzle—Hide box until they work the puzzle.

Outdoor games—croquet, badminton, baseball, etc.

Exercise equipment (See *Gift Ideas: Fitness Buff*)

Biorhythm charts or kit

Tickets to special sports or entertainment event

Book of passes to movie, ice cream parlor, bowling alley, miniature golf, etc.

Membership in dinner club (1 free meal for 1 bought)

Membership in Young Men's (or Women's) Christian Association, community
or recreation center, swim club; local museum, opera, symphony society
Membership in local educational television station (so they can receive month-
ly program listings.)
Loose-leaf address book
Toll-Free Digest (Warner Books, 1979). Directory of 17,000 toll-free telephone
listings.
Telephone amplifier
Telephone extension or decorator telephone
Gift certificate from telephone company
Bulletin board, memo board
Tape dispenser, desk organizers, pencil sharpener, pencil holder (See *Things
to Make*)
Big school bell (to call the kids home)
Bird feeder, bird house, bird bath
Wind chimes
Porch swing, hammock
Beach umbrella
Lawn furniture
Barbecue grill (See *Gift Ideas: Cook—Outdoor Cook,* for other ideas)
Picnic equipment—Thermos® jug, ice chest, basket, ground cloth
Hanging basket, pot plant, terrarium
Tree, shrubs, bulbs, or rose bush for yard
Pet door
Water purifier or replacement filters for it
Smoke detector, fire extinguisher
Automatic timer for lights
Door peephole, deadbolts
Fireproof lock box
Energy-saving devices—sun screen, weather stripping, storm windows, etc.
Small appliance—ice cream freezer, yogurt maker, popcorn popper (See
Appendix: Small Electric Appliances)
Fireplace equipment (See *Gift Ideas: Fireplace Gifts*)
Radio, clock, TV, video game or home computer program
Linens for bed, bath, kitchen, table
Photo album, photo wheel, film
Composite picture frame
Family tree: picture composite, narrative, outline, genealogy charts (filled in)
Assemble a family cookbook—all the relatives' favorite recipes.
Make a home movie of your family and other family members to send those
who live far away.
Holiday ornament or decoration
Alternative Celebrations Catalogue, Alternatives, Box 1707, Forest Park, Ga.
30051. $5. Thoughts and suggestions on making holidays less commercial.
Join Smithsonian Family Learning Project, Smithsonian Institution, Box 28,
Edgewater, Md. 21037. $11 for 12 months. Once a month they receive
directions for a science project for the whole family to enjoy.

Reader's Digest Back to Basics (Reader's Digest, 1981). "How-to" book on traditional American skills in homesteading, gardening, camping, crafts.

Make a throw pillow or wall hanging; embroider hand towels.

Make something with your hobby—ceramic bowl, woven place mats, wooden bookends, etc.

Coupons for babysitting, car wash, yardwork, etc.

Homebaked goods; preserves, pickles, jelly, etc.

Box of fruit, candy, cheese, meats, nuts

Gingerbread house, specially decorated cake

Matching T-shirts, nightshirts

Case of their favorite soft drink or prepared food (i.e., pork 'n beans or macaroni and cheese dinners)

Farewell Gifts

Box of tissues

Something local to remember the area by—playing cards or note paper with local scene; picture, area craft, T-shirt with local slogan

Subscription to local paper

Subscription to old or new area magazine

Address book—Put your name in!

Change-of-address post cards

Give an open house for them.

Bulbs for new yard

Flower pot (empty)

Wind chimes

Potted plant delivered by florist after they arrive in new residence

Write a note and mail it so it will be waiting at new house for them.

Stained glass window ornament

Muslin or autograph pillow signed in permanent ink by their friends

Collection of photos of good times together; photograph album

Stationery—maybe, with new address

Return address labels with new address

Have them for a meal on moving day or a few days before.

Babysit on moving day.

Friendship quilt or patchwork pillow—each square by a different friend.

Fireplace Gifts

Fire screen or kind with glass door
Pay for visit from chimney sweep.
Andirons, indoor wood rack
Tools—tongs, poker, brush, turner,
    broom
Bellows
Wood splitter, cord of wood
Long-handled popcorn popper,
    special fireplace grill
Fireplace matches,
    colored flame makers

Fisherman

When buying gifts for a fisherman, keep in mind the kind of fishing he does—fly fishing, deep sea fishing, surf fishing or lake fishing. See also *Gift Ideas: Outdoors* and *Boater* categories.

See *Catalogs: Boating* for sources.

Gift certificate to local fish market
Subscription to fishing magazine (see *Magazines: Outdoors*)
Book on fishing
Gift certificate to sporting goods store or catalog
Tickets to boat show, recreational vehicle show
Pay fee for fishing guide for a day at favorite lake.
Pay entry fee for fishing tournament.
Fish cookbook
Smoker (for cooking his catch)

Fish mounting kit
Ice chest
Insulated spillproof mug, Thermos®,
    canteen
Pocket camera, weather radio
Fishing chair, stool
Rod, reel, electric fishing reel, fishing
    line
Rod or reel carrying case; rod rack
Fishing rod holder, belt caddy
Live bait tank, bait bucket
Fisherman's vest

Tackle box, fly or lure box
Fishing pliers, fish hook remover, hook sharpener, hone, folding scissors
Pocket scales, stringer
Lures, baits, spinners, flies or kits to make them

Box of assorted hooks, weights
Knives—scaling, filet, floating, pocket
Floating key case
Floating or waterproof flashlight
Small first aid kit, air horn
Plastic tube for holding maps, leaders
Fighting belt (for bringing in the "biggies")
Fisherman's float; landing net, creel
Wading staff, wading boots, hip boots
Stream thermometer
Head-net hat, sunglasses
Rain gear, emergency blanket

Fitness Buff

Whether your friend exercises for fun or for her/his figure, you will find an idea for her/him below. Also see *Gift Ideas: Runner,* or other sports categories. Catalogs offering some of these items are listed under *Catalogs: Health & Beauty.*

Subscription (See *Magazines: Health & Fitness*)
Book on biofeedback, stress reduction, family medical guide, yoga, meditation, exercise, aerobics
Membership in health spa, swim club, YMCA or YWCA
Warm up suit, terry bathrobe, sports bra, leotard
Jumprope

Exercise mat, inclined exercise bench
Doorway gym bar
Doorway punching bag
Gymnastics ball
Rebound jogger
Stationary bicycle or stand for converting regular bicycle into one
Barbells, ankle weights
Digital watch, pedometer, stop watch
Bathroom scale
Tape or record of aerobic dance or exercise music
Padded innersoles for shoes
Tote bag for taking clothes to gym
Blood pressure monitor, first aid kit
Shower massage, heat massage
Dietary food scale
Water filter for faucet
Dust masks
Air purifier or "smokeless ashtray" for home or office
"No Smoking" sign or desk plaque, perhaps hand-painted or needlepoint
Jackie's Diet & Nutrition Charts, Jacqueline Hostage (Betterway Publications, 1982)

Gardener

These suggestions are for those who love house plants, patio tomatoes, or rows of vegetables so neat they could grace a nursery catalog cover.
Gifts sources can be found under *Catalogs: Gardening.*

Subscription (See *Magazines: Gardening*)
Gift certificate to local nursery or gardening catalog
Stationery, jewelry, pictures, hand towels, etc. with flower or vegetable designs
Farmer's or garden almanac for coming year
Book on plant care, gardening, organic gardening, local area gardening, flower arranging
Next Whole Earth Catalog (Random House, 1980)
Jackie's Indoor/Outdoor Gardening Charts, Jacqueline Hostage (Betterway Publications, 1982)
Several seed packets or bulbs in flower pot tied with gingham ribbon
Fruit or other kind of tree
Bulbs, bedding plants, seeds of all kinds
Potting trays, potting soil
Soil test kit
12-24-12 fertilizer, garden gypsum, superphosphate, organic fertilizers
Compost bin
Tool bucket or carry-all
Tools—trowel, gardening fork, clippers, pruning shears, dibble (punches holes for planting)
Cordless grass trimmer
Rake—expanding or regular
Weed puller, pruner on rod
Harvest basket
Wheelbarrow
Garden gloves, sun hat, knee pads, rubber boots
Garden hose, hose hanger, hose nozzles
Sprayer
Sprinkler—Some have automatic timer and cut-off.
Watering can—rustproof, large capacity
Underground irrigation system
Moisture meter, rain gauge
Plastic markers for plant identification
Humorous markers for garden, e.g. "Chipmunk Crossing"
Tomato supports, frames
Garden tower, multi-tiered garden
Cold frame (to cover plants in cool weather)
Greenhouse
Canning jars, lids, labels, equipment
Tube of liniment

Decorative Items

Wind chimes
Bird bath, bird feeder, bird seed, bird house
Bronze decorative faucets
Garden sculpture
Topiary
Hanging basket, plant hangers (indoor and outdoor)

Indoor Gardening

Mister, indoor watering hose, humidifier, small watering can
Humidity tray
Plant light
Ceiling track for hanging baskets
Plant dolly (dish on casters), plant display stand
Vase, decorative pot or planter—copper, brass, ceramic, clay, etc.
Terrarium

Flower Arranging

Books on technique, preserving flowers
Vases; silver or other centerpiece bowl with frog
Flower cutters, clippers; assorted flower holders

Golfer

For sources, see *Catalogs: Outdoors, Sports.*

Tickets to professional golf tournament
Golf lessons; book on golf
Subscription (See *Magazines: Sports*)
Take a movie of his golf swing for him to analyze.
Golf clubs, golf club covers (knit, crocheted, drawstring)
Golf club care kit
Golf bag, bag strap pad, bag on wheels, bag cart, bag rain
　　gear
Identification tag for golf bag—needlepoint, maybe
Golf umbrella, seat cane
Golf shirts, shoes, gloves
Dozen golf balls, tees
Ball and tee pouch (attaches to belt)
Golf ball monogrammer
Golf ball retriever, shag bag
Score card holder
Golf towel—personalized
Electric putting cup, home putting green and cup
Golf practice net
World's Worst Golf Jokes, Martin Ragaway (Price Stern, 1972)

Grandparents

These gifts are suggested with grandparents of young children in mind although many would be welcome from older children as well. Of course, items from other gift categories should be considered also.

Keep a photograph album all year and give it to them at the end of the year.

Picture frame, photograph album, photo wheel

"Brag book"—purse-sized photo album

Pictures—wallet-size, school, family, portrait

Make a collage plaque (see *Things to Make*).

Draw a picture or write a poem or story for them.

Write a "book." Have children write about some things they enjoy doing and illustrate their stories.

Send a taped letter.

Call, visit, or write them often.

Coupons for yard work, housecleaning, other chores

Ornament for Christmas tree with grandchild's picture and date or one the child has made.

Cookie jar or see *Things to Make: Coffee Can Cookie Jar*

Stitchery pictures, e.g. "If mother says no, ask grandmother."

Bumper sticker or plaque—"Ask me about my grandchild(ren)."

The Greatest Gift Guide Ever—especially for those who live far away and may not know child's interests

A Grandparent's Book, James Wagenvoord (HP Books, 1981). Lovely book with questions for grandparents to answer about their childhood, family traditions and other personal memories for the grandchild.

Groomsman

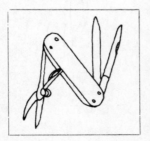

Silver or crystal jigger

Bottle of wine

Pewter tankard

Pocket knife

Bookends

Wallet, money clip

Belt buckle, cuff links, tie tack

Key ring

Necklace, bracelet—only if he wears jewelry

Man's jewelry box or dresser top organizer

Fountain pen and pencil set, letter opener

Record, tape or book

Handicapped

A gift for a handicapped person depends, of course, upon the kind and degree of disability. Many ideas can come from other interest categories in this book. Listed below are some useful supplies available for these people's special needs. Also see *Gift Ideas: Visually Impaired, Hearing Impaired, Nursing Home Resident* or *Elderly at Own Home* categories.

In the catalog section, see *Handicapped, Hearing Impaired* or *Visually Impaired.*

Take a person out shopping, to entertainment event, to restaurant.

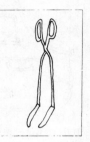

Prepared meals
Shopping bag on wheels, folding shopping cart
Portable cane seat
Wheelchair carry-all
Wheelchair beverage carrier
Coaster or ashtray that snaps onto wheelchair or bed railing
Bedside pouch
Lap desk
Telescoping magnet, reaching tongs
Foot mop
Card shuffler, card holder
Arm for holding telephone receiver
Remote switch for TV, lamp, etc.
Automatic page turner
Doorknob opener
Elastic shoelaces; stocking or sock pull-on
Front closure lingerie, clothing
Harness for one-handed fishing

Safety Aids
Portable raised toilet seat
Safety arm rest for toilet
Power failure security light
Bath tub safety rail
Bath chair, bath lift
Railing for outside steps

Kitchen Helpers
Pan handle holder
Curved butcher knife
Swivel eating utensils
Suction-base food chopper, grinder
Serving cart with casters
Mounted jar opener

Handyman

Handymen can specialize in plumbing, electrical work, carpentry, automotive repair, or other areas. The tools are specialized and too numerous to list. Here are some ideas for the man or woman who tries a little of everything.

Sources are found under *Catalogs: Books, Craft Supplies—Woodworking, Electronics* and *Handyman.*

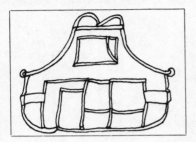

Subscription to do-it-yourself magazine (see *Magazines: Handyman*)

Gift certificate to hardware store or catalog or lumber yard

De Cristoforo's Complete Book of Power Tools, R.J. de Cristoforo (Harper and Row, 1973).

Encyclopedia of Hardware, Tom Philbin (E.P. Dutton, 1978).

Other books on repairs or special interest area

Tuition for course in automotive repair, cabinetwork, etc.

List of plumbers or electricians who make emergency calls

Toolbox, multi-drawer cabinet

Pegboard for hanging tools; shelves in workshop

Tool pouch, nail bag, carpenter's apron

Heavy-duty work gloves

Heavy-duty extension cord

Ladder, saw horses

For shop: workbench, broom, paper towel holder, waterless hand cleaner, fan, heater

Level

Drill, attachments

Sander, assorted grades of sandpaper

Saws—handsaw, jigsaw, sabre saw, etc.

Miter box

First aid kit for shop

Caulking gun, soldering gun, staple gun

Power tape measure, flexible ruler

Good paint brushes, rollers, paint pans

Assorted sizes of nails, screws, washers, nuts, picture hangers, bolts, wire

Tools—screwdrivers, hammers, wire-cutter pliers, tin snips, jeweler's screwdriver, utility knife, pipe wrench, channel lock, contour gauge, C-clamps, etc.

Box of household adhesives—super glue, masking tape, electrician's tape, duct tape, silicone sealer, epoxy, Elmer's® glue, wood glue, weather-strip adhesive, etc.

Antique or unusual tools

Hearing Impaired

Those who do not hear or who have trouble hearing have most of the same interests and wants as those who hear well. Here are a few special items they also might appreciate.

See *Catalogs: Hearing Impaired.*

Course in lip-reading

Subscription to *Deaf American* (see *Magazines: Hearing Impaired*)

Items such as books, T-shirts, stationery, mugs, poster, etc. with sign language on them

Aid-o-phone (to carry to use on a telephone)

Vibrator wake-up device or alarm clock

Clock with flashing lights

Sentry or sound lamp—device hooked up to react to the sound of the doorbell, TV, baby crying, etc.

Telecommunication machine—teletypewriter attached to telephone that transmits to similar machine on another telephone

Telephone amplifier

Personal television amplifier (enables television sound to remain at normal level for others in room)

American Sign Language, Martin L. A. Sternberg (Harper & Row, 1981). Comprehensive dictionary.

High School Graduation

This is a time of achievement, celebration, new beginnings. From high school, paths lead to college, an apartment, a job, marriage, independence. Think of the student's future plans when selecting a gift. You may want to consult *Gift Ideas: Adult (Basic), Men, Women, Bachelor, Single Woman, Wedding, College Student Away From Home, Housewarming, Cook* or area of special interest.

A job offer

Frame for diploma

Portrait of graduate or frame for it

Give a party.

Class ring

Gift certificate for two to nice restaurant
Passes to movie, bowling, miniature golf
Tickets to special entertainment or sports event
Special trip
Luggage, travel kit, heavy-duty clothes bag, tote bag
Camera, film
Photograph album, scrapbook
Address book, stationery
Autograph book, pillow
Typewriter
Dictionary; *Roget's International Thesaurus* (Harper & Row, 1979); book
    of famous quotations; other reference book
Book of etiquette—a modern version if you want it used!
Sylvia Porter's New Money Book for the 80's, Sylvia Field Porter (Avon, 1980)
The Only Investment Guide You'll Ever Need, Andrew Tobias (Harcourt Brace
    Jovanovich, 1978).
Passages: Predictable Crises of Adult Life, Gail Sheehy (E.P. Dutton & Co.,
    1974).
Other books on adult development, money management, self-improvement,
    time management
The Greatest Gift Guide Ever
Bookends; handmade, personalized or silver bookmarks; bookplates
Magazine subscription

Desk accessories and organizers, pencil sharpener, pen-
    cil holder, pen and pencil set
Cash, savings bond; add to savings account.
Wallet
Clothing—lingerie, sweaters, T-shirt with personal
    slogan, robe, pajamas, nightgown
Umbrella—folding or automatic
Anything with emblem of chosen college
Watch, jewelry, jewelry box
Start a silver flatware set for her.
Radio, clock radio, non-electric alarm clock
Pocket calculator
Cassette recorder or player, stereo
Record, tape, record or tape holder
Personal care appliance (see *Appendix: Small Electric Appliances*)
Iron, travel iron
Sewing kit, sewing machine
Linens for bed or bath
Humorous laundry bag
Beach towel
Small ice chest, Thermos®, picnic equipment

History Buff

Determine in which period or country your historian friend is interested—American Civil War, early English, Renaissance, World War II, etc. Then look for something on this list from that period of history.

Tickets to place of interest (national monument or historical site)
An item from the period such as documents, coins or currency, stamps, buttons, clothing, glassware, art objects
Book or periodical published during the period
Book about the period
Subscription (see *Magazines: History*) or single issues of magazines that deal with the period
Biographies of people who lived during the period

Famous autographs or maps from the period
Art that depicts the period
Copies of crafts or decorator items of the period such as dolls, pioneer toys, clock, needlework, quilt, dishes, furniture, candlesticks, jewelry
Family history or family tree (filled in as much as possible)
Copy of newspaper or magazine from her day of birth, or coins or stamps from year of birth
Tape of radio program, speech or music from the period
Copy of old newsreels
Book on the history of his town or area
Tape or notes from old family members on family anecdotes, events, members, memories

Host-Hostess

Some people love to have company by twos or by twenties. If you don't find a gift idea under *Cook,* look here for fancier, easier serving ideas. See also *Gift Ideas: Bar Gifts* and *Silver Gifts.*

Catalogs carrying appropriate merchandise are listed under *Catalogs: Housewares, Gifts,* and *Food.*

Book of party games; bridge tallies or score pads
Personalized or assorted invitations, note cards or post cards
Dinner bell
Guest book
Guest soap, soap dish
Assorted cheeses, mints, coffees, jellies, relishes
Favorite wine, liquor
"No Smoking" sign—needlepoint, painted, wooden
Smoke eliminator, ashtrays, air purifier

Linens
Cocktail or dinner napkins—permanent press or linen
Make coasters out of quilted material
Place mats, tablecloth, table runner, matching napkins
Guest towels, pretty towel holder
Pillows

Decorations
Vase
Flower arrangement—china, fabric, wood, dried
Fresh flowers
Candlesticks, candelabra, candle, Uncandle®
Ice sculpture art molds

Beverage Aids

Glassware, mugs
Coasters
Coffee urn, espresso or cappuccino maker
Pitcher
Decanter set, liquor labels
Insulated vacuum server
Punch bowl, cups, ladle
Wine rack, wine cooler
Ice bucket, tongs
Wooden stemware holder
Demitasse cup set
Ice crusher—manual or electric

Serving Accessories
Snack set (small trays with cups); dessert set
(same with pitcher)
Decorated paper plates, matching paper napkins and cups
Paper party napkins—initialed or printed with name
Serving dishes
Serving trays (all sizes)—silver, wood, enamel, plastic, painted
Warming tray, 1- or 2-burner buffet range
Electric plate warmer
Hors d'œuvre knives or forks, cocktail forks
Steak knives, carving set
Cake or pie serving knife
Grapefruit or melon spoons
Trivets
Lazy Susan
Napkin rings
Salt shaker, pepper mill
Molds
TV trays, card table, folding chairs, serving cart

Special Function Dishes

Cruet
Small dishes for relishes, mints; condiment server
Cheese board, knife; cheese saver with cover
Chip and dip set
Bread basket
Cookie jar
Cake plate
Salad bowl, salad servers, individual bowls, salad stand
Soup tureen
Chafing dish
Casserole dish—Oven-to-freezer is useful.
Gravy separator
Parfait glasses, sherbets, banana split dishes

Housewarming

When friends move into a new home, it is traditional to take them a gift when you first visit the house. When choosing the gift, consider whether this is a first home, a new house, or a new town.

Some gift sources are listed under *Catalogs: Home Furnishings, Housewares, Gardening* and *Smorgasbord.*

List of reliable repairmen, doctors, 24-hour grocery or drugstore nearby
Take pictures of house in various stages of completion and present to new owners.
Offer to paint.
Take prepared meal or have them for a meal several days before or after moving.
Gift certificate to hardware store
Change-of-address cards
Return address labels or stationery with new address

Book on home energy conservation, home repair, do-it-yourself projects, local gardening information
Subscription to home decoration or home improvement magazine (see *Magazines: Women,* or *Handyman*)
Free Things for Homeowners, Yolande Flesch (Cornerstone, 1981)
Free Stuff for Home & Garden (Meadowbrook Press, 1981)

On Moving Day

Keep the children.

Take them a picnic lunch; have them over for a *quick* meal.

Take a cooler of drinks, cookies or fruit.

Lend a strong back.

Take an emergency kit of Band-Aids, paper towels, paper cups, soap, toilet paper, scissors, dust rags, all-purpose cleaner, pen and note pad, anything they might need and can't locate.

Outside Ideas

Front door plaque with family's name

Front door knocker

Mailbox—decorated or with family's name

Door mat—personalized

House numbers for door or lawn

New or decorated garbage can, garbage can caddy

Outdoor bell to call kids home

Lawn furniture

Potted plant or hanging basket

Tree, shrubbery, flowers, bulbs, grass seed, rose bush

Safety Devices

Door peephole, dead bolts, door chain, window locks, door alarm

Automatic light timer

Smoke detector, fire extinguisher, fire escape ladder

Fireproof lock box

Indoor Ideas

Bath set, towels, guest towels

Fancy soap—scented, initialed, shaped

Candles

"No Smoking" sign—hand painted, needlepoint

Ashtrays

Vase

Wine rack, bottle of wine

Personalized cocktail napkins

Collection of light bulbs

Guest book

Closet organizers

Fireplace equipment (see *Gift Ideas: Fireplace Gifts*)

Wall decoration—plaque, picture, stitchery, macramé hanging

Toolbox, assorted tools (see *Gift Ideas: Handyman*)

Broom, mop, bucket

Assorted nails, screws, picture hangers, wire

Household adhesives—masking tape, super glue, epoxy, electrician's tape, etc.

Hunter

In choosing gifts for a hunter, keep in mind what he hunts, the time of year he hunts, and what he hunts with. Other ideas are in *Gift Ideas: Outdoors.* See *Catalogs: Outdoors & Sports.*

Gift certificate to sporting goods store or catalog
Tickets to gun show, recreational vehicle show
Smoker for cooking his kill
Glasses, mugs, picture, print, dishes with hunting motif
Mounting plaque for horns, head, birds
Subscription (see *Magazines: Outdoors*)
Books on weapons, hunting, wildlife
Detailed map or aerial photo of hunting area—Check with highway department or Agriculture Stabilization and Conservation Service (ASCS) office in county where land is located.
Weather radio
Campstool with pockets
Small first aid kit
Hunting knife
Stainless steel, wide-mouth Thermos®
Canteen that doesn't rattle or shine
Ice chest
Game bag

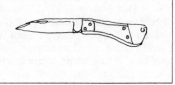

Clothing
Thermal underwear
Rainsuit or poncho
Camouflage suit
Fur-lined cap or gloves
Shooting gloves, shooting mitt with flap for trigger finger
Shooting glasses
Socks—heated or wool

Gun Equipment
Gun cleaning supplies
Gun case, gun sling
Ammunition or reloading equipment
Scope
Gun safe for home
Gun rack for truck, home

Bird Hunter
Bird bag
Decoys
Bird dog, dog grooming aids, book or kit on training dog to retrieve
Calls—duck, goose
Duck blind

Archer
Bow, bow strings, bow case
Quiver, arrows
Gloves, finger tips, finger tabs, arm guard
Arrow straightener, fletching tools, kit for making arrows
Broadheads, small game points
Target, matt, easel, 3-D target
Bow and arrow rack

III Persons

When you want to cheer up a friend in the hospital or at home, choose something from this list or the appropriate age category in the children's section.

Book satchel to hang on side of bed; bed caddy, Vogue pattern #2006 or Butterick pattern #4371; fabric bag to tie to hospital bed railing
Fill bag with little gifts for each day—lipstick, cologne, playing cards, dry shampoo, baby powder, hand lotion, toothbrush, pencil and note pad, small book, card, small toys
Small bell to ring when he needs something
Pajamas, gown, robe, tennis socks (to wear in bed), washable slippers
Shawl
Cute bed sheets, pillowcases
Soft pillows in cheerful fabric—14-in. square or 9 × 18-in., stuffed with thin layer of polyester filling
Light reading, tape, record, magazine or newspaper
Cards, cards, cards—include cartoon or funny clipping or make a card with words appropriate to the situation cut from magazines.
Shallow basket for card holder
Take roll of masking tape to hospital so patient can tape cards on wall.

Crossword puzzle book
Game for one or two, bingo, playing cards, checkers
Book of solitaire card games
Lap desk
Bed tray
Prop-up pillow
Personalized cup, mug, glass, plate
Colorful or seasonal paper napkins for bed tray
Bring patient's favorite ice cream, gelatin, custard, etc. or basket of fresh fruit (with doctor's permission).
Take a party to hospital—colorful napkins, silver flatware, special food (depending on patient's diet).
Bouquet of fresh flowers from your garden in a container

Especially for Children
Activity book
Richard Scarry's Best Make-It Book Ever (Random House, 1977).
Comic book or other book
Art box—coloring books, tablet, crayons, scissors, glue, tape, colored pencils
      and pens, pipe cleaners, etc.
Origami book and paper
Felt Box (see *Things to Make*)
Puzzle
Paper dolls, doll, stuffed animal or see *Things to Make: No-Sew Doll*
Autograph pillow or animal for visitors to sign
Little guest book or gift list
Catalog or old pattern book to cut up
Doodle-Art® poster, paint-by-number kit, art kit
Spirotot®, Spirograph® (Kenner)
Hand puppet
Kaleidoscope
Xylophone
Small cars, toys
View-Master®, reels

Just a Little Something

Sometimes you want "just a little something" to give a friend to say, "Thanks,"
"I like you," or "I'm glad you're my friend." Here are some ideas for special
remembrances.

Candle, scented or meaningful shape; candleholder
Box of note cards, pretty post cards, stationery, funny
      memo pads
Holder (hand-decorated) for pencils, rings, tissue, let-
      ters, etc.
Bridge tallies or score pads
Scented, shaped, or initialed soaps
Hand towel, apron
Homemade goodies—cookies, molded salad, cake, pie,
      bread, pickles, casserole
Plate of shaped cookies plus the cookie cutter
Favorite wine or liquor
Box of fruit, cheese, teas, candy
Mix recipe of spiced tea and put in a decorated tin, good storage container,
      pretty jar.
Gift from your garden

Potted plant, flowers, hanging basket, flower pot
Fabric or china flowers
Favorite record or book
The Greatest Gift Guide Ever
Long-distance phone call
Seasonal decoration
Jewelry—initialed, stick pin, earrings, necklace, bracelet, pendant
Personalized key ring
Decorated tin box
Figurine or small print reminding you of the person
Write a note telling what her friendship means to you.

Lefties

When someone comments that a lot of things are not right in this world, he may be a pessimist—or he may be left-handed!

If you are right-handed and have ever tried using scissors with your left hand, you will understand the problems of lefties in accomplishing many simple, everyday tasks.

The following items can be found with handles or openings reversed or otherwise altered for left-handed use. Check *Catalogs: Lefties.*

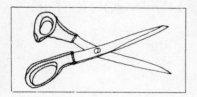

Pitcher, mug with handle on right
Zipper pull
Scissors, pinking shears
Pocket knife, screwdriver
Belt buckle
Wallet with billfold on left when change purse is upright
Kitchen knives, corkscrew, utensils, ladle, can opener, vegetable peeler, ice cream scoop, measuring cup
Fishing reel; catcher's mitt; fielder's glove; golf, bowling or tennis glove; archery bows
Playing cards with numbers in all four corners
Camera with shutter button on left
Watch that winds on left
Spiral notebooks, checkbook bound on right
Left-handed ruler numbered right to left
Lefty T-shirt, mug, note paper, tote bag, bumper sticker
Manuals on left-handed craft work, golf, calligraphy, guitar, teaching left-handed children, etc.
Lefthanders International, 3601 S.W. 29th St., Topeka, Kan. 66614.
    Membership, $15 per year. Magazine, product information, etc.

Men

Here are a few ideas that do not fit neatly into any other category. For many more suggestions, see *Gift Ideas: Bachelor, Adult (Basic),* and appropriate interest categories.

Belt buckle, belt caddy
Tie, neckscarf, tie rack
Shirt—sport, dress, knit
Handkerchiefs—Monograms are nice,
    but no-iron fabric is nicer!
Travel kit
Calendar filled in with family's or
    friend's birthdays, anniversaries
Cosmetics, cologne, after-shave lotion
Valet
Jewelry—neck chain, bracelet, cuff
    links, watch, ring, tie tack

Book on being a man today, fatherhood, male "mid-life crisis"
Plaque or stitchery saying, "Anyone can be a father, but it takes someone special to be a daddy."
Coupons for yard work, car wash, etc.
Reclining chair
Subscription (see *Magazines: Men*)

Mentally Ill

Persons in a mental institution have needs similar to those in a full-care nursing facility (see *Nursing Home Resident*). They need basic clothing, personal care items, and sometimes household equipment. Check with each institution for regulations and individual needs.

Fresh fruit, homemade cookies, cake
Non-perishable food—peanut butter, crackers, nuts, candy, gum, packages of punch or tea
Nutcracker
Paper cups and dispenser
Party napkins, favors
Any clothing item which is easily laundered—robe, pajamas, dress, socks, bathing suit, shorts, slacks, slippers, sweater, raincoat, underwear, shawl, head scarf, etc.
Make-up or cosmetics of all kinds, comb, brush, mirror
Soap, soap dish

Toothbrush, toothpaste
Wheelchair robes, caddy
Jewelry, jewelry box
Purse, wallet, coin purse, tote bag
Hair curlers, hair dryer, hair nets, curler bag,
   ribbons, barrettes
Hanging basket, gardening tools, gloves, seeds,
   potting soil
Books, magazines, newspaper subscription
Posters, pictures, bulletin board, plastic flowers,
   anything to brighten the room
Wall clock, ashtray, lamp, throw pillows
Art supplies—paper, paints, felt markers, scissors, pencils, glue, etc.
By-number painting kits, needlecraft kits, decoupage kit, bird feeder kit
Sewing notions, fabric, patterns
Tools—hammer, nails, screwdriver, wood chisel, saw, pliers, etc.
Outdoor games—horseshoes, jumprope, volleyball, baseball, croquet, etc.
Indoor games—bingo, checkers, puzzles, cards, etc.
Musical instruments—guitar, harmonica, etc. with instruction books
Song books, record player, records
Assorted greeting cards, stationery, stamps, pencils, pencil sharpener
Holiday decorations
Television or radio

Mentally Retarded

"The mentally retarded are more like the rest of us than they are different," persons who work with them stress.

Gifts for the mentally retarded should, in most cases, be age appropriate. Usually choose the concrete (the hands-on) over the abstract. Children enjoy the same kinds of toys (unless very complicated) and clothing fads as other children. For mentally retarded adults, select gifts (perhaps on a simpler level) as you would for anyone else.

Musician

Gifts for musicians are as diverse as the instruments they play. These ideas can be adapted to please people with different musical talents.

See also *Catalogs: Music.*

Lessons
Metronome, pitch pipe
Music stand
Antique instrument
Tickets to concert or musical program
Tape a recital or program he performs in.
Gift certificate to music store or catalog
Caricature of musician using art prints or magazine picture and inserting face of your friend.
Carrying case for instrument, identification label
Brief case for music
Book on famous artist in friend's favorite medium
Subscription (See *Magazines: Music*)
Record in particular field of interest—organ, jazz, flute, etc.
Blank cassette tapes, tape holder
Record stand
Holiday sheet music, record, tape
Head phone that plugs into electric guitar, organ
Music dictionary
Collections of music—book-record combinations
Pencils, staff paper
Decoupage or collage of programs he has participated in
Custom designed program for a special recital
Scrapbook of programs, recitals over a period of time
Laminate or frame a piece of music the person wrote or is special to her.
Things with musical symbols—jewelry, note paper, picture, tote bag
T-shirt reading "Magic fingers" or some other slogan
Miniatures of instrument, musician, director
Sheet music—Old copies are interesting gifts.
Old or antique hymnal for a church musician
Choral musician—Membership in Chorister's Guild, 2834 W. Kingsley Rd., Garland, TX 75041
Pianist—Piano tuning, piano lamp, needlepoint piano bench cover
Guitarist—extra set of strings, variety of picks, guitar strap, cords, capo
Drummer—percussion instruments, sticks, practice pad

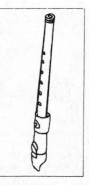

Needleworker

Just as artists differ from housepainters, needleworkers differ from seamstresses. They have similar skills, but use different equipment. Since some ideas overlap, see *Gift Ideas: Seamstress.* This category encompasses many specialties—needlepoint, stitchery, knitting, crewel, latch-hook, crochet, quilting, etc.

Good sources are listed under *Catalogs: Craft Supplies—Needlework* and *Craft Supplies—General.*

Kits to make
Subscription (see *Magazines: Crafts*)
Gift certificate to needlework store or catalog
Tote bag or storage basket for current project
Lessons in specialty, pattern books
Reader's Digest Complete Guide to Needlework (Reader's Digest, 1979).
Frame or make a pillow from a picture she worked.
Embroidery hoop, needles, thread assortment
Crewel needles
Good shears, folding scissors
Yarn palette (for separating yarn by color)
Magnifying glass
Tatting shuttle, thread
Blocking board
Thimble, needle threader
Tracing wheel, tracing paper, design transfer equipment, hot iron transfers
Knitting: needles, circular needle, stitch and row counter, bobbins, stitch holder, point protectors, ring markers, yarn-end weaver, cable stitch needle, gauge ruler and knitting needle measure
Crochet: Set of hooks, big cone of crochet cotton
Needlepoint: frame for working pieces; non-bleeding markers
Quilting: quilting frame or hoop, quilting scissors, quilting needle, water-erasable marking pen, leather thimble with metal tip, templates for patterns

New Parents

Some people prefer giving gifts like these, directed more to the new parents than to the baby.

Parent's Book, James Wagenvoord (HP Books, 1981). Thoughts, reflections, hopes for a child. Questions for parent to answer.
Sterling silver diaper pin for proud Mama to wear
Family genealogy with baby's name included

Diaper service
"Cents off" coupons for paper diapers
Coupons for babysitting
Maid service once a week
Frozen meals for when they are too tired to cook
Take dinner to them.
Cabinet door latches, caps for electrical outlets,
  door gate
Loan parents big baby equipment.
Rocking chair

T. A. for Tots, Alvyn M. Freed, PhD. (Jalmar
  Press, Inc., 1974). Transactional analysis
  for and about children.
Book on parenting, e.g. *How To Parent,* Dr.
  Fitzhugh Dodson (Nash Publishing, 1971);
  Children: The Challenge, Dr. Rudolf Dreikurs (Hawthorn Books, 1964);
  Parent Effectiveness Training, Thomas Gordon (New American Library,
  1975); *Between Parent and Child,* Haim G. Ginott (Macmillan, 1965);
  Dare to Discipline, Dr. James Dobson (Bantam Books, 1981); *Practical
  Parenting Tips,* Vicki Lansky (Meadowbrook Press, 1982).
Free Stuff for Parents (Meadowbrook Press, 1980)
Subscription to parenting magazine (see *Magazines: Lifestyle*)
Potted plant, tree or rose bush
Film, photograph album, picture frame

Nursing Home Resident

The greatest number of inquiries for gift ideas were for people in this category,
yet it was one of the simplest lists to make. One reason may be that many people
fail to understand the special needs of someone in a full-care facility. With
household functions provided, a large number of gift ideas are automatically
eliminated. The items most nursing home residents want or need often are so simple
we may feel that "it isn't enough."

When choosing a gift, consider the resident's disabilities (like visual impairment
or paralysis) and interest (for some older people, reading is too tiring). Remember
also that table display space is limited and that many local fire regulations do not
allow plastic items in nursing homes. Most of all, keep in mind that your presence
is worth much more than your presents.

For active or ambulatory residents, check *Gift Ideas: Retirement Home Resident* or other interest categories for more ideas. See also *Handicapped, Visually
Impaired* and *Hearing Impaired.*

Special sources are listed under *Catalogs: Handicapped, Hearing Impaired* and
Visually Impaired.

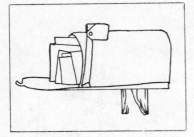

Subscription to hometown or church newspaper

Individual magazines, rather than subscription

Large-print books or magazine (see *Magazines: General Interest* for *Reader's Digest, Large-Type Edition*)

Request greetings for birthday or anniversaries from mayor, governor or President (see *Gift Ideas: Anniversaries,* for details.

Go Christmas caroling at the home (Children's voices are especially welcome) and take simple refreshments (if allowed).

Visit often even if the patient doesn't respond to your visit. Sometimes the patient receives better care if the nursing home staff knows someone checks in frequently.

Install private telephone.

Telephone often.

Send a taped letter.

Plan a trip out of home (if allowed) for dinner, show, visit at family's home.

Decorate the room for a holiday—Check home's fire regulations. Plastic and paper decorations are often banned.

Give a small party in the nursing home.

Take a picnic lunch to eat on the patio.

Do his shopping for him.

Anything made by children or grandchildren or made especially for her

Photo wheel with lots of family pictures

Small bulletin board—Change items on it frequently.

Wheel chair caddy or carrying bag

Folding TV or bedside table on wheels

Lap desk, pens, pencils

Lighted magnifying glass

Assorted greeting or holiday cards with stamped envelopes

Note paper, pretty post cards with stamps

Wall calendar with large numbers, pretty pictures, moon signs

Pretty decoration for wall

Fresh flowers in vase, small potted plant, hanging basket

Cassette recorder; radio, television with earphones—Put permanent identification on it or check it with desk.

Pretty pillowcases

Lap robe, synthetic sheepskin throw

Soft, washable blankets

Washable foam rubber cushion and side pillows for chair or wheelchair

Washable bedroom slippers

Personalized labels for clothing—sew-on, not iron-on kind

Handkerchiefs, box of tissue

Toilet articles, bath powder, room fresheners, body lotion, cologne, after-shave lotion

Crossword puzzle books, dominoes, playing cards, bean bag toss

Box of hard candies in sealed container

Homemade food (with permission) in metal tin to keep it fresh (Plastic containers are often against fire regulations.)

Fresh fruit (with permission)—bananas, grapes, any easy-to-eat fruit

Coin purse with coins—Take a few each time rather than leaving a lot. Coins "disappear" easily.

Box of flexible straws

For Women

Lacy, back-closing hospital gown

Front-opening wash-and-wear dress, brunch coat, robe, nightgown

Hose—knee or ankle length

Jewelry

Shawl

Zipper pull

For Men

Pajamas, robe, socks, house slippers

Sports shirt (pull-on)

Wash-and-wear cardigan sweater

Tie, tie tack, belt, wallet with plenty of photo space (include photos)

Outdoors

People who spend lots of time outside—whether camping or hunting or hiking—share similar needs. When selecting a gift from this list, consider the type of outdoor activity and the normal temperature. For other, more specific ideas, see *Gift Ideas: Backpacker, Boater, Camper, Cyclist, Fisherman* or *Hunter*. Gift sources are listed under *Catalogs: Outdoor & Sports*.

Membership in Sierra Club, Box 7959, San Francisco, Cal. 94120. Regular member, $25/year. Student, junior (thru 14) and senior (60 and over), $12.

Subscription (see *Magazines: Outdoors*)

Books on birds, wildlife, first aid, snakes, trees, wild flowers, stars, trails, campsites, adventurers, solar cooking

Roger Tory Peterson's field guides to animal tracks, birds, shells, butterflies, mammals, reptiles, rocks, trees, insects, wild flowers, stars

Audubon Society field guides to insects, butterflies, birds, seashore creatures

Topographic quadrangle maps from U.S. Geological Survey, 1012 Federal Bldg., 1961 Stout St., Denver, Colo. 80294. Write for list of maps.

Glasses, mugs, picture, print, jewelry, notecards, T-shirts with outdoor motif
Make first aid kit in small plastic box—disinfectant, adhesive tape, sterile cotton or gauze, aspirin, burn and chap ointment, insect repellant, folding scissors, first aid book, Band-Aids, pre-moistened tissues, instant cold compress.
Survival kit in light backpack—waterproof matches, candle, map, compass, 100 ft. strong fishing line or copper wire, dehydrated food and beverage, signal mirror, whistle, antiseptic bandages, reflective blanket, cup, parka or poncho, extra socks, knife.
For children—bright red or yellow jacket or shirt (easy to spot), whistle.

Clothing
Embroidered or hand-painted denim shirt
Parka (hooded is nice), poncho
Warm socks (top quality virgin wool, synthetic/wool blend), electric socks
Boots, tennis shoes, snowshoes; boot jack
Electric footwear drier
Light cotton work gloves, leather gloves, removable wool glove liner
Hand warmer
Bandanna, wool scarf
Warm hat, sun hat, head net (to keep bugs away)
Good quality sunglasses
Insulated or fishnet underwear
Rainsuit—Nylon coated with Neoprene is first rate.
Down-insulated vest, jacket
Wool shirt or jacket, chamois shirt
Wool or heavy-duty pants, jeans
Beachwear—suit, cover-up, beach towel, beach bag

Eating Equipment
Flat G.I. can opener
Thermos®, ice chest, (collapsible) water jug
Box of large trash bags
Swiss Army Knife or pocket knife—carbon steel or stainless steel blades
Folding drinking cup
Dried food, beverages
Waterproof matches
Wild game or outdoor cookbook
Portable grill
Nesting cookware, dishes
Picnic basket
Insulated canteen or vacuum server
Solar oven, solar tea jug

Other Useful Equipment
Compass, range finder
Binoculars
Pocket camera, camera harness, watertight camera bag

Pocket barometer-altimeter, wind chill meter, wind speed meter
Camp stool with pockets, folding chair
Mosquito net, fly swatter
Cot, hammock, sleeping bag, tent
Ensolite® pads (light, water resistant), air cushion or mattress
Stuff bag, equipment bag, tote bag (nylon or waterproof)
Waterproof tarp
Beach umbrella
Picnic blanket (washable)
Space blanket, all-weather blanket
Waterproof flashlight
Fluorescent lantern
Rope hoist
Air horn, signal mirror
Repair kit—sturdy needles with large eyes, a few yards of strong nylon or
    Dacron thread, thin fishing line, small roll of copper wire, nylon repair
    tape, polyethylene tape for mending any surface
Waterless hand cleaner

Person Living Abroad

Gifts for military families, overseas personnel with big companies, or missionaries abroad involve more than just selecting an appropriate item. The sender must check customs regulations for the country to which the presents will be sent and estimate the postage to determine whether the gift is worth sending at all. Your local post office can help with both of these questions. Sometimes, especially in the case of military personnel who have Post Exchange privileges, it is easier to send money and let the receiver buy the gifts. However, some things cannot be found overseas and are welcomed by Americans living abroad. (See other gift categories also, being conscious of weight in selecting an item.)

Subscription to hometown newspaper
Subscription to American magazine
English language books
Familiar brands of cosmetics, toothpaste, soap,
    cigarettes

Food or other items not available there (Toilet
    paper is one commonly mentioned.)
Packages of dried food—spaghetti sauce, chili
    seasoning mix, etc.
Small tape player
Tapes from family, friends
Tape a game of a favorite sports team.
Pictures from home
Electric current converter

Air mail stationery
Dictionary of the language of the country (cross-referenced with English)
Homemade cookies (bar kind that won't crumble) or candy (kinds that last
    a long time) packed in airtight coffee cans
T-shirt (especially for children) that says, "I am a foreigner. I speak only
    English."
    Spanish—Estoy extranjero. Hablo solamente ingles.
    French—Je suis un étranger. Je parle seulement l'anglais.
    Italian—Sono straniera. Parlo solo inglese.
    German—Ich bin Aauslander. Ich spreche nur englisch.

Photographer

This category lists gift suggestions for people who just take snapshots and for those who develop and print their own pictures. Be sure to find out the kind of camera and the size and type of film used. For dark room supplies, know the type of printing done (black and white or color) and favorite brands of chemicals.

Look under *Catalogs: Photography* for sources.

Subscription (See *Magazines: Photography*)
Book or manual on technique, special effects, developing, exposure, film, etc.
Photograph album, picture frame
Negative and slide files, sleeves, pages
Film, flashbulbs
Prepaid mailers for film developing
Gift certificate to photography store
Camera bag, case—large enough for extra lenses, film accessories
X-ray-safe film bag for travel
Camera strap, harness
Projection screen
Slide projector, slide trays, sorter, editor, lighted viewer
Movie projector, reels, film editor, splicing tape
Slide or movie title lettering set
Filters—all kinds (need to know lens size)
Light meter
Lens (know camera size and model); lens hood, lens case, lens cleaner
Tripod
Camera bracket
Small strobe unit, movie light
Slave trigger for strobe
Bounce head (for bounce flash), flash extension cable
Cable release cord
Cropping guide

Darkroom Equipment

Developing chemicals—Find out what brand he uses.
Chemical storage containers
Developing trays, tanks, reels
Film-changing bag
Film washer
Photo paper dispenser, photo paper
Photo texturizing kit, texture screens
Paper trimmer
Dry mounting materials
Darkroom lamp, safelight
Enlarger, enlarger lens
Focusing cloth
Automatic enlarger timer
Digital darkroom timer
Contact printer
Enlarging easel

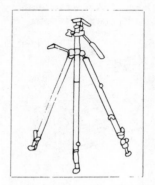

Print drier
Slide ready mounts
Color processing or slide processing equipment, chemicals, thermometer
Kit or chemicals for making prints from slides
Cotton gloves, sponge tip tongs
Water filter
Automatic tray siphon
Automatic print washer
Darkroom graduate (for measuring)
Loupe, magnifier
Print squeegee
Film clips
Dodging kit, burn-in kit, vignetter
Re-usable film cartridges, bulk film loader
Accessory drying rack
Retouching colors, equipment

Retirement Home Resident

A retirement home is like an apartment unit for senior citizens with a central kitchen. Most residents are active, alert, and still able to do most things for themselves. Therefore, many of your gift ideas will come from *Adult (Basic), Men, Women* or special interest categories. Some ideas from *Nursing Home Resident* or *Elderly at Own Home* categories are appropriate also.

Take person out for dinner, movie, entertainment.
Magazine subscription
Large print books, Bible, magazine (see *Reader's Digest, Large-Type Edition*)

Books, religious music, or Bible study on tape (see *Catalogs: Visually Impaired*)

Bookmark (Make one!)

Request greetings for birthday or anniversary from mayor, governor, or President (see *Gift Ideas: Anniversaries*).

Small refrigerator
Hot plate
Toaster-broiler
Small coffee pot
Linens, afghan
Quilt with children's and grandchildren's names on squares
The Greatest Gift Guide Ever
Terrarium
Restore or copy old photos; photo wheel
Decorator telephone
Stained glass window ornament

Holiday door decoration

Tape player-recorder or stationery to keep in touch with family or friends

Small TV, radio, clock radio

Runner

Perhaps this list will jog your memory for some good gift ideas.

Identification tag (with any medical information)
Subscription (See *Magazines: Running*)
Books on running technique, philosophy, aerobics
Massage oil, liniment
Hour's paid massage at spa
Jogging suit or shorts, sports bra
Reflective clothing
Knitted cap, gloves for winter jogging
Visor
Athletic socks

Shoe laces, key holder that attaches to shoe laces
Slogan T-shirt
Sweatbands—wrist and head
Leg weights
Jogging shoes, heel repair kit
Pedometer
Digital stop watch
Neck towel—monogrammed
Wrist radio or earphones

Non-spill water pitcher or Thermos®, small ice chest

Gatorade®

Scuba Diver

If your scuba diver rents his equipment, you may want to give him or her some item from the Basic Equipment list. If he owns his gear, he probably can use something from the Accessories list.

Subscription to diving magazine (see *Magazines: Water Sports*)
Books on diving, underwater world
Diving lessons
Underwater camera equipment
Spear fishing equipment
Gift certificate to diving equipment store
Waterproof wallet
Waterproof duffel bag, gear bag

Accessories
Diving watch
Wet suit shampoo
Wet suit gloves, boots, hood
Mask strap, fin strap, knife strap
Snorkel lock
Rubber marking paint
Defog solution
Rubber preservative
International "Divers Below" flag for
  boat
Catch bag

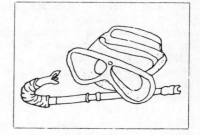

Basic Equipment
Wet suit, gloves
Depth or pressure gauge, compass, thermometer, console for gauges
Hose protector
CO_2 cartridge for air device
Cylinder, backpack, regulator
Mask, fins, snorkel
Buoyancy compensator
Diving vest
Repetitive dive charts
Underwater lights
Safety whistle
Diver's knife
Hooks, buckles for belt
Weight belts, weights

Seamstress

For those who do more than put in hems and sew on buttons, there are many handy gadgets and accessories that make their hobby (or chore!) easier. See also *Gift Ideas: Needleworker* if the seamstress you know appliqués or embroiders the pieces she sews. See *Catalogs: Crafts—Needlework* or *Crafts—General.*

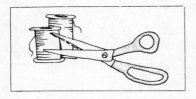

Sewing machine
Attachments for sewing machine— buttonhole maker, decorative stitches, etc. (Know model number and make of machine.)
Subscription (see *Magazines: Crafts*)
Books on sewing, tailoring
Lessons in sewing—many phases and skill levels
Personalized labels—"Made for you by..."
Gift certificate to fabric store
Gift certificate for sewing machine cleaning or scissor sharpening
Length of material (up to 2 yards for child, 3 yards for adult)
Sewing kit, thread box
Good quality scissors, pinking shears, or shears for cutting knits or nylon
Body form
Cutting board
Long wall mirror
Pin cushion—wrist type or make one
Silver or decorative thimble
Steam iron

Useful Gadgets

Tape measure, metal yardstick , curved measuring gauge
Tailor's chalk, marking pencils, tracing paper, tracing wheel
Hem marking clips, hem marker on stand
Box of new pins, ball-point pins for knits
Hem-bonding tape
Press mitt, press ham, sleeve board
Point turner
Seam ripper
Knit fabric mender
Baste-and-sew glue
Body ruler pattern fitter, pants pattern fitter
Pattern storage box—Decorate it yourself.
Travel sewing kit
Extra bobbins
Needle threader, assortment of needles
Assorted colors of good quality thread
Little boxes to hold pins, snaps, buttons, etc.

Silver Gifts

For weddings, anniversaries or special occasions, some people want to give "anything just so it's silver." Here are suggestions. Most of these items are also available in pewter.

Jewelry—spoon ring, charm, pendant, bracelet, earrings, chain, pin, stick pin, cuff links, tie tack, medallion, rings
Belt buckle
Pendant or cross out of woman's silver pattern
Comb and brush set
Baby items—teething ring, cup, eating utensils, jewelry
Picture frame; cigarette box, lighter
Flower pot, bud vase, centerpiece with frog
Trivet; napkin rings
Antique silver items
Silent butler; candelabra, candlesticks
Casserole with removable glass liner
Covered vegetable dish, serving dishes
Trays, bread tray
Water goblets, wine glasses; jigger
Revere bowl, compote, candy dish, relish dish
Jelly dish with spoon
Cream and sugar set
Gravy boat, butter dish
Flatware, steak knives, carving set (For hard-to-find or discontinued silver or silverplate flatware patterns, see *Catalogs: Housewares—Walter Drake Silver Exchange*)
Demitasse spoons, pastry set, dessert plates
Tree meat platter
Coffee service, tea service
Christmas tree ornaments
Bell
Trinket box

Single Woman

These items seem particularly suited for a woman living alone. Like bachelors, single women really appreciate things made especially for them. Be sure to check *Gift Ideas: Adult (Basic), Women* and special interest categories.

Deadbolts for doors, door peephole, door alarm, door chain
Automatic timer for lights
Smoke detector, fire extinguisher
Small whistle on necklace, hand-held siren for purse

Big flashlight, batteries
Course in karate, self-defense, rape prevention
Basic course in auto or home repairs
Names of trusted auto mechanic, repairmen
Membership in American Automobile Association (check local phone book
    or see *Gift Ideas: Traveler* for address) or other travel club that has emer-
    gency road service.
CB radio for car
Jumper cable or locking gas cap for car
Book of coupons for car wash, yard work, etc.
Book of tickets to theater, bowling, ice cream parlor, miniature golf, etc.
Two tickets to sporting or entertainment event

Take her out for dinner.
Have her over for dinner.
Single serving meals for freezer
Books on hobby, money management, adult
    development
The Greatest Gift Guide Ever
Jar opener
Step stool
Anything made just for her—throw pillow, pic-
    ture, work shirt, needlepoint purse, etc.
Anything personalized—T-shirt, mug, jewelry,
    key ring, beach towel, tote bag, etc.
Linens
Popcorn popper, small coffee pot, etc. (see *Ap-
    pendix: Small Electric Appliances*)
Tuition for leisure course—photography, scuba diving, gourmet cooking, etc.
Lessons in disco or ballroom dancing
Money
Cosmetics
Potted plant, terrarium
Take her photograph; paint her portrait.
Write her a song, poem.
Personalized car license plates
Magazine subscription
Small TV, radio, alarm clock
Wine, candy, flowers, record, book, tape
Holiday ornaments or decorations
Card table, chairs
Dishes, glasses for entertaining
Barbecue grill, ice chest, picnic basket
A pet

Snow Skier

Some items are for the avid skier while others are useful also for first-timers. Find gift sources under *Catalogs: Outdoors & Sports.*

Subscription to skiing magazine (see *Magazines: Snow Sports*)
Books on skiing
Knit cap, ski mask, wool scarf
Ski gloves, leather mittens, waterproof gloves, glove liners
Goggles, sunglasses with wind visor and green or yellow lenses
Ski boots, boot bag, boot tree, hiking boots, after-ski boots, snow gaiters
Heavy socks, sock liners, knee socks, leg gaiters
Long underwear, thermal underwear
Sweater—turtleneck or other kind
Stretch pants, insulated ski pants, warm-up suit
Flannel slacks, blazer, sport jacket, shirt
Parka, nylon windshirt
Ski bag
Fanny pouch, belt pouch
Wine bota (flask)
New poles, skis
Book of ski lift tickets
Ski lock, ski ties or carrier
Car rack for skis
Ski wax kit
Lip and sun cream

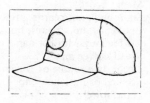

Sports Fan

Whether your sports fan goes to the games or parks in front of (monopolizes) the television set, you can find something on this list for him or her.

Tickets to sporting event
Book on major sports figure, sports records
Subscription (see *Magazines: Sports*)
Baseball cap
Stadium seat or cushion, stadium blanket
Thermos®, small ice chest
Binoculars
Small TV, TV antenna, transistor radio with
    earphones
Sports equipment
Anything with team's logo on it—T-shirt, jacket, mug, notebook, cap, waste-
    basket, memo pad, pennant, license plate frame, bumper sticker
Key ring, jewelry, figurine, or small print or picture relating to favorite sport
See also *Catalogs: Sports—Pro Team Corner.*

Teacher

Sometimes students want to thank a special teacher with a gift at the end of the year or on a holiday. Here are some favorites. Check *Gift Ideas: Desk Dweller* and *Just a Little Something* categories for other suggestions.

An appreciative note

Gift of money to school, designating that it be used for teaching aid chosen by your teacher for her room.

Give book to school library in her name.

Book on his favorite subject (new or very old book)

The Greatest Gift Guide Ever

Stickers, balloons, certificates to use as class awards

Magazine subscription in her subject area

Stained glass decoration for window

Sand painting

Small potted plant

Pretty cookie tin or tray full of cookies

Candy or condiment dish

Pretty basket filled with fresh fruit, homemade cookies, bread

Anything from your garden or kitchen

Any craft you do well

Decoupage a tissue box or letter holder.

Desk top or drawer organizer, tape holder, pencil holder

Stapler, staple remover, box of staples

Big box of #2 pencils, ball point pens, felt tip pens, red pens or pencils

Fountain pen to hang around neck

Personalized pencils

Desk picture frame

Cute note pads

Memo board

Stationery, note cards, pretty post cards

Bookends, bookplates, bookmark

Coffee mug with her name on it

Set of coffee mugs

Decorative candle or Uncandle®

Scented or initialed soap

Hand towel

Stick pin, bracelet, pendant, neck chain, earrings

Holiday decoration or ornament you made

Personalized tote bag

Tennis Player

Your tennis fan will "love" any of these gifts. You can find some items in *Catalogs: Outdoors & Sports.*

Tickets to tennis tournament
Take a movie of his playing for him to study.

Tennis lessons
Subscription to tennis magazine (see *Magazines: Sports*)
Book on tennis technique
Racket, racket cover (needlepoint or handmade)— McCall's pattern #7378
Can of tennis balls, tennis ball belt
Hanger for racket and balls—fits on clothes rod
Tennis bag
Tennis trainer—base with ball on string
Practice rebound net
Tennis press
Tennis socks, shoes
Tennis hat, cap with visor
Tennis glove
Tennis shorts, skirt, dress, panties
Warm-up suit
Sweatband—head or wrist
Small ice chest, Thermos®
Kit for stringing or re-gripping a racket

Traveler

A traveling businessman or vacationer would appreciate a gift from this list.

Give a bon voyage party or host a picture show after traveler's return.
Subscription (see *Magazines: Travel*)
Book on part of world he likes (or hopes) to visit
Road atlas, current highway map
Passes to nearby museums, national parks, etc.
Golden Eagle Passport—$10 per vehicle, good for one calendar year for admission to any national park, monument, area. (Golden Age Passport— free with proof of age over 62.) Can be purchased from Public Inquiry, National Park Service, Washington, D.C. 20240 or at any federal area where fees are charged.
Literature on national parks from National Park Service (address above) or on national forests from Dept. of Agriculture, Forest Service, Box 2417, Washington, D.C. 20013.
Coupons for house sitting—watering plants, feeding pets, checking mail, etc.

Membership in travel club or American Automobile Association, 8111 Gatehouse Rd., Falls Church, Va. 22042. (Check local phone book for local office.) Benefits include emergency road service, touring information, insurance, etc.

Toll-Free Digest, free telephone listings—see *Gift Ideas: Adult (Basic)*

Free Stuff for Travelers, Bruce Lansky (Meadowbrook Press, 1981)

The Best Free Attractions, John Whitman (Meadowbrook Press, 1982)

National Budget Directory, Pilot Books, 347 Fifth Ave., New York, N.Y. 10016. $3.50. Published every April. Lists budget motel chains in U.S.

U.S. and Worldwide Travel Accommodations Guide, Teachers Tax Service, 1303 E. Balboa Blvd., Newport Beach, Cal. 92661. $5.95. Lists more than 200 universities offering dorm rooms for summer travelers at about $6–12 a night.

Rand McNally National Park Guide, 1982.

Let's Go, Budget Guide to the USA, Harvard Student Agencies (St. Martin's Press, 1982)

Bed & Breakfast USA, Betty Rundback et al. (E.P. Dutton, 1982). Guide to tourist homes and guest houses.

Country Inns and Back Roads, Norman Simpson (Berkshire Traveller Press, 1982). The first and best guide to country inns.

Travel diary, small address book

Photograph album

Slide trays, slide sorter, slide viewer

Camera, film, pre-paid film mailers

Camera bag, X-ray-safe film bag

Childen's travel games (see *Things to Make: Felt Box*)

Book on crossword puzzles or word games or paperback for next trip

Waterproof (also leakproof) cosmetic kit

Make a drawstring laundry bag.

Package of travel detergent, inflatable clothes hangers, elastic clothesline

Portable iron

Travel sewing kit

Clothes brush

Shoeshine kit, shoe mittens (cloth bags for shoes)

Luggage, men's shaving kit, tote bag, clothes bag

Luggage identification tags, personalized luggage straps

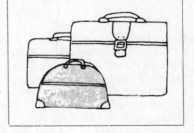

Luggage handler—enables carrying two suitcases easily in one hand

Luggage wheels, collapsible luggage cart

Folding umbrella

Folding jewelry tray or bag

Hanging baby seat (for restaurants)
Weather radio
Portable combination lock or burglar alarm for hotel door
Automatic light timers to leave at home—Get one for radio, too.

Car Traveler

Automobile burglar alarm
Car first aid kit
Driving gloves
Commuter mug—insulated, spill-proof
Insulated beverage holder
Thermos®, insulated vacuum server
Small ice chest
Coffee console—plugs into car lighter
Car snack tray, car wastebasket or caddy
Car visor organizer
Car window shade
Car vacuum
Car clothes bar
Luggage rack with cover
Folding snow shovel
Emergency reflector blanket
Fire extinguisher
Flashlight—small enough for glove compartment
Trunk or hood light
Flare, signaling wheel cover
Mileage counter and timer
Children's games, tapes (for tape deck or portable cassette player)
Auto compass
Cassette adapter—lets you play cassettes in 8-track system
Personalized hood ornament

Foreign Traveler

Foreign language course, records, or cassettes
English-foreign language dictionary
Sight-seeing guide, travel guide—Arthur Frommer's or Fodor's guides are
    good.
Envelope of coins in the foreign currency so he will have change for tips when
    he arrives
Small cloth pouch (hangs around neck) to hold passport, traveler's checks
Voltage converter
Painting or art print of place she's been

Things To Make

Carry-all's—McCall's pattern #7583 or Butterick #4105
Cosmetics case, jewelry case—McCall's patterns #7842 and 7378
Jewelry roll, traveler's tray—Vogue patterns #1528 and #1753
Shoe socks (drawstring bags for shoes to fit in)

Vegetarian

Also check *Gift Ideas: Cook* and *Gardener*

Juicer
Yogurt maker
Food dehydrator
Flour, grain, seed mill
Mortar and pestle for grinding
Canning and food processing equipment
Crock pot
Soup bowls, soup tureen
Vegetable steamer

Food slicer, grater; food processor
Herb garden, sprout kit, patio tomato plant
Dried fruit, nuts, honey
Nut bowl, nutcracker
Basket of fruit, fruit bread
Corn or pea sheller
Salad spinner
Cookbooks such as *Laurel's Kitchen, A Handbook of Vegetarian Cooking & Nutrition,* Laurel Robertson et al. (Bantam Books, 1981) or *Home Food Systems,* Roger B. Yepsen, Jr. (Rodale Press, 1981)—methods and tools for producing, processing and preserving naturally good foods.

Visually Impaired

Visually impaired persons enjoy basically the same activities as sighted persons, so check *Gift Ideas: Adult (Basic), Men, Women,* or other appropriate interest or children's categories. The items below have been specially adapted for those who cannot see or cannot see well and who rely greatly on their sense of touch. Those whose blindness is a result of diabetes, however, cannot use the Braille or raised dot markings on many of these items. For children, strive for a variety of textures, sizes, shapes, and sounds. (See *Catalogs: Visually Impaired* for sources of these items and others.)

Talking books, Braille books, books on tape
Children's Braille books, Scratch and Sniff books, touch and feel books
Subscription to Braille magazine (see *Magazines: Braille*)
Braille Book Review, National Library Service for the Blind and Physically Handicapped, Library of Congress, 1291 Taylor St., N.W., Washington, D.C. 20542. Write for free list of Braille books and magazines available through libraries.
Book stand
Greeting cards in Braille

Braille or large-print playing cards or table games such as Monopoly®, Scrabble®, Chinese checkers

Beep ball (electronic beeping system inside), audible ball (with bell inside)

Special sports equipment for visually impaired

Toys—musical, smooth wooden, stuffed, Nerf®

Cassette recorder, tapes

Variable speech control recorder-player

Records, Braille or large-print sheet music

Light sensor, audicator, print locator, light detector

Lighted magnifier

Braille compass

Braille ruler, tape measure—with tactile indicators

Modified automotive gauges, equipment

Talking calculator or electronic calculator with Braille print-out

Braille counter

Braille or large-print labeling equipment

"Free Matter for the Blind" rubber stamp

Braille slate, paper

Signature guide, writing guide, envelope addressing guide

Braillewriter

Large-print telephone dial or touch-tone phone attachment

Watch, clock, alarm clock with raised dots

Talking alarm clock

Talking or large-print thermometer

Magnetic padlock

Smoke detector

Kitchen timer, pots, blender, mixer, etc. with raised dots on controls

Slicing guides for cake, pie, bread, meat

Cake caddy—cuts and lifts triangular piece of cake

Electronic liquid level indicator

Braille cookbook

Automatic needle threader

Sock sorter

Aluminum clothing tags—to indicate colors

Bath tub safety bars

Bathroom scale with raised dots

Water Skier

See also *Gift Ideas: Boater*

Subscription (see *Magazines: Water Sports*)
Lessons
Beach towel, swim suit, suit cover-up
Water ski wet suit
Skis, slalom ski
Water ski case
Athletic eyeglass holder
Ice chest
Thermos®, insulated beverage holder

Wedding

Wedding gifts used to be the easiest gifts to buy because brides traditonally needed everything. However, with more people marrying later in life (or marrying more times), a beginner's household list is not always appropriate for gift suggestions. The ideas below supplement those found in *Gift Ideas: Host-Hostess, Cook, Housewarming, Family,* and *Silver Gifts.*

Offer to take wedding pictures, snapshots or movie at reception.
Tape the ceremony.
Make the rice bags.
Address wedding invitations.
Give a dinner or party.
Make bridal gown.
Make hors d'œuvres or wedding cake or cater the wedding.
Make Pacific cloth bags with Velcro® closures for silver pieces.
Make traditional garter.
For outdoor summer wedding, party or reception, make heart-shaped fans (white posterboard edged in wedding color and glued to tongue depressor).
Bride's book
Frame wedding picture or invitation.
Family Bible
Wedding plaque with wedding date and couple's names in needlepoint, stitchery, or paint.
Make wedding bells—Cut 18 in. high out of white satin, burlap or felt. Trim in satin ribbon, lace and pearl beads. On one, bead or embroider names of bride and groom. On other, put the wedding date. Display with satin rope.
Send champagne to honeymoon spot.
Anything in couple's chosen patterns—stainless flatware, sterling flatware, everyday or china dishes, crystal stemware

Silver knife for cutting wedding cake
Anything in sterling or silverplate (see *Gift Ideas: Silver Gifts*)
Jewelry—necklace, pendant cross in bride's silver pattern, pin, bracelet, locket
Home decorations you make—photograph, needlework pillow or picture, painting, stained glass, etc.
Bed pillows
Pillowcases—satin, monogrammed, embroidered with couple's name
Bed and bath linens (monogrammed), table linens
Blanket (Find out bed size); electric blanket (dual control)
Handmade quilt
Holiday decorations
Recipe scrapbook from family, friends
Recipe box with your favorite recipes inside
Matching bath sarongs, robes, pajamas
Stationery with new name (and address if couple will be there at least a year)
Silver chest
Zippered storage bags for china
Candlesticks, candelabra—wood, silver, pewter, brass, crystal
Two silver, crystal, or pewter goblets or champagne glasses
Set of glasses (see *Gift Ideas: Bar Gifts*)
Small elecric appliance (see *Appendix: Small Electric Appliances*)
Picture frame, photograph album
Camera, film
Vase, flower pot, potted plant
Spice rack—already stocked
Laundry basket full of kitchen utensils, staples, paper and cleaning products
Clock radio, wall clock, alarm clock
Small TV, radio, stereo, tape recorder-player
Vacuum cleaner
Sewing machine
Ironing board, iron
Frame photographs of bride and groom as children.
Anniversary candle
Book on etiquette, household hints, money management, adult development, marriage
The Greatest Gift Guide Ever
List of birthdays, anniversaries, names of relatives on both sides of family
His and her tool sets
Card table, folding chairs, TV trays
Lingerie
Stock the medicine cabinet—thermometer, heating pad, Band-Aids, ice pack, disinfectant, etc.
Card file and 3 × 5 cards for recipes, addresses, wedding gift record, etc.
Address book

Wedding Showers

Here are several kinds of showers and a few gift ideas to get your thinking started. Refer also to *Gift Ideas: Cook, Housewarming, Host-Hostess, Adult (Basic)* and *Handyman* for more ideas.

Appliance shower—See *Appendix: Small Electric Appliances*

Bathroom shower—Linens, towel holder, hand mirror, scented soap, soap dish; medicine chest items, thermometer, heating pad; cleaning items; plumber's friend

Couple shower—Two of anything (pillowcases, matching T-shirts, robes, pajamas, His and Her mugs, towels, bath sheets, etc.)

Embroidery shower—At the party, guests embroider their names or design on dish towels, quilt squares, cocktail napkins, etc.

Freebie shower—Things a couple collects only with time (rags, empty jars or plastic storage containers, free cookbooks, good recipes)

Groom's shower (couples or men only)—Tools, handyman books, pajamas, robe, heavy-duty extension cord, yard equipment (see *Gift Ideas: Gardener, Handyman, Men*)

Kitchen shower—Small electric appliance (see list in *Appendix*), utensils, dish towels, cookbooks, cookware, aprons, staples, storage containers (see *Gift Ideas: Cook*)

Linen shower—Towels (hand, bath, kitchen, guest), wash cloths, blanket, bed linens (check bed size), pillows, mattress pad, place mats, tablecloth, napkins, hot roll cover, bath set

Lingerie shower—slip, panties, gown, robe, slippers, lounging gown, hose, bra

On-the-go shower—Gift certificates to movies, restaurant, bowling alley, theater, miniature golf, sporting event, etc.

Pantry shower—Canned goods (with or without their labels!), staples, cupboard organizers, paper goods

Paper shower—Paper towels, napkins, toilet tissue, shelf paper, place mats, plates, cups; cookbooks, handyman books, household hints book; *The Greatest Gift Guide Ever*; wedding book; stationery, magazine subscription; photo album

Pot Luck shower—Guests bring food to eat and leave the bride and groom the recipe and serving dish.

Recipe shower—Guests bring a favorite recipe and at least one ingredient (non-perishable) in it.

Spice shower—Guests bring a bottle of spice and a recipe using it.

Trousseau shower—Linens, clothing, or jewelry for bride

Ideas For Any Kind of Shower

Centerpiece—Spray paint a small tree branch and anchor in flower pot filled with pebbles. With ribbon, attach whatever is appropriate to the theme of the shower—measuring spoons, thermometer, napkin rings, spools of thread, etc.

Shower souvenir—Make or buy a plain muslin pillow piped in a color. With permanent marking pens, write name of honoree and date of shower. Decorate it as you wish and have guests sign it.

Western

For some folks, Western wear is a costume. For others, it's a way of life. The first grouping of gift suggestions should please either kind of cowboy or cowgirl. The working cowboy and rodeo rider have extra needs. Look under *Catalogs: Western* for riding equipment, Western clothes and gifts with horse motifs.

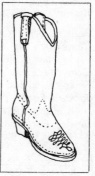

Western shirt, jeans, vest, chambray shirt, jeans jacket
Western hat, hat band
Boots, boot socks, boot shaper, boot jack
Belt buckle, silver or fancy belt tips or belt keeper
Western, turquoise jewelry
Bola tie, oblong neck scarf
Engraved boot tips or heel scallops
Ladies' square dancing shoes, dress
Snuff box cover
Suit bag with pocket for boots
Anything out of denim—skirt, purse, book cover, tote bag, etc.
Western art
Picture, lamp base, desk accessories with horse or ranch motif
Country music album or tape
Sun screen or decorated mud-flaps for pick-up truck
Subscription to horse or riding magazine (see *Magazines: Horses*)
Books on the West, horses, ranching, horsemanship
Wrap gift in a bandanna.

Working Cowboy or Cowgirl

Rain slicker
Deerskin gloves
Chaps
Roping can, new ropes
Practice steer head
Bridle, halter, head stall or breast collar for horse
Favorite kind of bit or tie down
Skid boots for horse

Saddle bags; saddle pad or blanket
Pocket knife
Portable spittoon (non-spill) for pick-up truck

Rodeo Riders
Belt holder
Bull riding glove
Resin bag
Rope pad, rope can
Stirrups, spurs
Rigging bag

Women

Most women's gift ideas are covered in other categories [see *Gift Ideas: Single Woman, Adult (Basic),* interest categories]. Here are a few extras.

Book on being a woman, mother, working woman
Cinderella Complex, Colette Dowling (Pocket Books, 1981). Best seller on "women's hidden fear of independence."
Color Me Beautiful, Carole Jackson (Ballantine Books, 1980). Find your best colors, styles.
Jackie's Book of Household Charts, Jacqueline Hostage (Betterway Publications, 1981)
Best of Both Worlds, Joan W. Anderson (Betterway Publications, 1982). Guide to full- and part-time home-based careers.

Coupons for babysitting, cooking, housework, etc.
Course in self-defense, rape prevention
Police whistle, tear-gas device for purse
Gift certificate to her favorite hairdresser
Needlepoint a purse or eyeglass case
Embroider, appliqué, or paint a design on a skirt or shirt.
Crochet an airy shawl.
Jewelry—a ring, necklace, neck chain, religious pendant, bracelet, earrings, watch
Ring box or holder, earring tree, jewelry box
Vanity tray, dressing table set, hand mirror
Tissue box—Hand-decorated ones are special.
Potpourri, sachets
Cologne, perfume
Cosmetics—body powder, bubble bath, bath oil, nail polish, soap
Comb, compact

Blouse, skirt, dress, shoes, handbag, gown, robe, pant suit, slip, sweater, scarf, belt, gloves
Subscription (see *Magazines: Women*)

Wood Hobbyist

Since there are hundreds of tools and gadgets for working with wood, find out what kind of woodwork he specializes in and ask a hardware store clerk about supplies for that particular kind of work. Here are some ideas that are general enough to please many specialists. See catalogs under *Catalogs: Craft Supplies—Woodworking, Handicrafts, Handyman,* or *Models & Miniatures.*

Book of patterns, ideas, techniques, tools in his specialty area
Subscription (see *Magazines: Handyman*)
Tuition for woodworking class at hobby store, community college
Gift certificate to hardware store, lumber yard, tool catalog
Small stickers reading, "Handcrafted for you by..."
Box of Band-Aids
Assortment of sandpaper, wood screws, nails, bolts, nuts, brads
Files, clamps, gauges, ruler, hammer, screwdrivers, pliers, vise-grip pliers, set of wrenches
Power tools—lathe, jigsaw, table saw, disc sander
Foot switch for power tools
Mitre box and saw
Hand plane
Good paintbrushes
Goggles, nose mask
Combination square
Molding cutter, scroll saw, inlay cutter
Wood carving tools—chisels, turning tools, carving knife
Tool sharpening stone
Miniature tool set
For workshop: good lock, paper towel holder, intercom or telephone extension, peg board and hooks
Precision ruler, caliper
Level
Heavy-duty extension cord
Heavy-duty vacuum cleaner
Soft, wide broom for sweeping up sawdust; dust pan
Storage cabinet with small, transparent drawers
Workshop apron

Writer

Give an autograph party for her new book.

T-shirt reading, "Ask me about my book."

Subscription to writer's magazine or magazine in specialty area (see *Magazines: Writing*)

Book on style such as *Manual of Style* (University of Chicago Press, 1969)

Book by or about admired author, about area of specialty

Book on writing markets—*Writer's Market* (Writer's Digest) is a good one, published yearly.

New dictionary, reference book

Roget's International Thesaurus (Harper & Row, 1979).

Bartlett's Familiar Quotations, John Bartlett (Little, Brown and Co., 1968).

Bound book with blank pages

Filing cabinet or boxes, file folders

Typewriter, typewriter ribbons (know brand and model of typewriter), correction tape or fluid

Coupons for manuscript typing

Letterhead stationery on 25% rag bond paper. Select business-like type. It could read, "Nancy Bell, writer." Give address (with Zip code) and phone number (with area code).

Watermark, 25% rag bond paper (white)

Legal pads, typing paper

Personalized clipboard

Bookends, bookplates, bookmark

Personalized address labels or #10 envelopes

Box of #10 envelopes or manila envelopes (9″ × 12″ or 9½″ × 12½″)

Rubber stamps—"Do Not Bend," "First Class," "Photos"

Postal scale

Roll of stamps

Index card file, index cards

#2 pencils, paper clips, pencil holder, pencil sharpener

Desk or drawer organizer

Desk lamp

Briefcase

Magazines

Magazine subscriptions are gifts that last all year.

Since over 25,000 periodicals are published in this country, it is impossible to list every magazine that may make a good gift. This list is a sampling of special interest magazines, their addresses and subscription prices. These prices, of course, may change at any time.

Subscriptions to foreign publications cost more. You can write each magazine for its foreign rates. Rates to overseas military addresses often are only slightly higher than domestic prices.

Where only a subscription price is given, the magazine publishes 12 issues a year. Other publishing schedules (number of issues per year) are noted after the subscription price.

Animals & Wildlife	Electronics, Audio, Video	Men
Antiques	Games & Leisure	Model Building
Arts	Gardening	Music
Automobiles & Vehicles	General Interest	Outdoors
Aviation	Good Reading	Photography
Boating	Gracious Living	Running
Braille	Handyman	Science
Children (thru teens)	Health & Fitness	Snow Sports
Collectors	Hearing Impaired	Sports
Computers	History	Travel
Cooking	Horses	Water Sports
Crafts	Lifestyle	Women
Cycling		Writing

Animals & Wildlife

Audubon, National Audubon Society, 950 Third Ave., New York, NY 10022
$16/6 issues
Cat Fancy, 8322 Beverly Blvd., Los Angeles, CA 90049 $11.97/8 issues
Cats Magazine, Box 83048, Lincoln, NE 68501 $14.50
Dog World, 300 W. Adams St., Chicago, IL 60606 $14
Freshwater & Marine Aquarium Magazine, Box 487, Sierra Madre, CA 91024
International Wildlife, National Wildlife Federation, 1412 16th St. N.W.,
Washington, DC 20036 $10.50/6 issues
National Wildlife, National Wildlife Federation, 1412 16th St., N.W.,
Washington, DC 20036 $10.50/6 issues
Off-Lead, Box 307, Westmoreland, NY 13490 $12 Dog training magazine.
Pets and People of the World, 1325 Chestnut St., San Francisco, CA 94123 $15
Ranger Rick's Nature Magazine (See *Magazines: Children*)
Your Big Back Yard (See *Magazines: Children*)

Antiques

Antique Collector, Freepost, London W1E 6EZ, England $30
Antique Trader Weekly, Box 1050, Dubuque, IA 52001 $19/52 issues
Antiques Journal, Box 1046, Dubuque, IA 52001 $11
Antiques World, Box 990, Farmingdale, NY 11737 $21.95/9 issues
Art & Antiques, One Worth Ave., Marion, OH 43302 $21/6 issues "American
magazine for connoisseurs and collectors."
The Magazine Antiques, 551 Fifth Ave., New York, NY 10176 $38
Spinning Wheel, Pegasus Ltd., 1981 Moreland Pkwy., Bldg. 4A, Annapolis,
MD 21401 $15/6 issues. "Magazine of antiques and early crafts."

Arts

American Artist, 1 Color Ct., Marion, OH 43302 $18
Art in America, 542 Pacific Ave., Marion, OH 43302 $29.95/10 issues
Artforum, Box 980, Farmingdale, NY 11737 $36/10 issues
Arts Magazine, 23 E. 26th St., New York, NY 10010 $33/10 issues
Dancemagazine, Box 960, Farmingdale, NY 11737 $22. Serious ballet.
Horizon, Box 517, Birmingham, AL 35201 $18/10 issues. Music, dance, arts.
Portfolio, Box 2716, Boulder, CO 80322 $15/6 issues. "Magazine of the Fine
Arts."

Automobiles & Vehicles

Auto Racing Digest, Box 4563, Des Moines, IA 50340 $5.95/6 issues
Car & Driver, Box 2770, Boulder, CO 80302 $11.98
Cars Magazine, Box 99, Amawalk, NY 10501 $13/10 issues
Four Wheeler, Box 2547, Chatsworth, CA 91311 $12.98

Hot Rod, Box 3293, Los Angeles, CA 90028 $11.94
Mini Truck, Box 2260, Costa Mesa, CA 92626 $15
Motor Trend, Box 3290, Los Angeles, CA 90028 $11.94
Petersen's 4 Wheel & Off-Road, Box 3289, Los Angeles, CA 90028 $11.94
Road & Track, Box 5331, 1255 Portland Place, Boulder, CO 80322 $15.94
Truckin', McMullen Pub., Box 2508, Santa Ana, CA 92707-0508 $15

Aviation

Air Classics, 7950 Deering Ave., Canoga Park, CA 91304 $14.95
Air Progress Aviation Review, 10968 Via Frontera, San Diego, CA 92127 $7.50/4 issues
Airpower, 10718 White Oak Ave., Granada Hills, CA 91344 $11/6 issues
Flying, Box 2772, Boulder, CO. 80302 $16
Homebuilt Aircraft, Box 28897, San Diego, CA 92127 $16.95
Plane & Pilot, Box 28897, San Diego, CA 92127 $16.95
Private Pilot, Box 2432, Boulder, CO 80322 $15.97
Ultralight Aircraft, Box 28897, San Diego, CA 92127 $16.95/12 issues
Wings, 10718 White Oak Ave., Granada Hills, CA 91344 $11/6 issues

Boating

Boating, Box 2773, Boulder, CO 80321 $18. Buying information, boating adventures.
Canoe, Box 10748, Des Moines, IA 50349 $12
Cruising World, Box 4295, Manchester, NH 03108 $18
Motor Boating & Sailing, Box 10075, Des Moines, IA 50350 $13.97
Motorboat Magazine, 126 Blaine Ave., Marion, OH 43302 $9.50
Powerboat, 15917 Strathern St., Van Nuys, CA 91406 $9
Rudder, Box 1159, Los Angeles, CA 90028 $15.94
Sail, Box 10210, Des Moines, IA 50336 $19.75
Sail Boarder, Box 1028, Dana Point, CA 92629 $12/6 issues
Sailing, 125 E. Main St., Port Washington, WI 53074 $12
Southern Boating, 615 S.W. 2nd Ave., Miami, FL 33130 $8
Trawler Cruiser Yacht, 524 Thames St., Newport, RI 02840 $10/2 issues plus 4 newsletters
Western Boating, 1440 W. Walnut, Box 7030, Compton, CA 90224 $15
Wooden Boat, Box 4943, Manchester, NH 03102 $15/6 issues
Yacht Racing/Cruising, 401 N. Broad St., Philadelphia, PA 19108 $18/10 issues
Yachting, Box 2704, Boulder, CO 80302 $18

Braille

More than 80 magazines are available free and mailed directly to eligible blind or handicapped persons through the National Library Service for the

Blind and Physically Handicapped (NLS) program. Contact the library network serving your area for details. The magazines are available in Braille, disc, cassette, or large type.

The program includes such popular titles as *Better Homes and Gardens, Jack and Jill, Fortune, Consumers' Research, Sports Illustrated, Farm Journal, National Geographic,* and *U.S. News and World Report.*

Available from Recorded Periodicals, Division of Volunteer Services for the Blind, 919 Walnut St., 8th Floor, Philadelphia, Pa. 19107 (Cassette—purchase $33.25/year; $16/year if cassettes are returned):

Boy's Life—Also in Braille.

Family Circle

Nature and Ecology—selections from such publications as *National Wildlife, International Wildlife, Sierra, Natural History.*

Omni—science fiction; futurism; UFO; space

Popular Science/Popular Mechanics

Saturday Review

Scientific American

Available from American Printing House for the Blind, 1839 Frankfort Ave., Louisville, Ky. 40206:

Newsweek—Disc

Reader's Digest—Free to eligible persons; Braille, disc.

Available from Reader's Digest Fund for the Blind, Pleasantville, N.Y. 10570:

Reader's Digest Large Type Edition—$10.95/12 issues.

For a complete listing of magazines available through loan or subscription or by direct mail, request a copy of "Magazines in Special Media" from Reference Section, National Library Service for the Blind and Physically Handicapped, Library of Congress, Washington, D.C. 20542.

Children (thru teens)

Bananas, Scholastic Home Periodicals, Box 1925, Marion, OH 43305 $8.95/ 10 issues. Ages 12–18. Humor.

Boys' Life, 1325 Walnut Hill Lane, Irving, TX 75062 $8.40. Ages 8–18. Boy Scout magazine, but non-Scouts can subscribe. Outdoors, experiments, sports, etc.

Child Life, Box 567, Indianapolis, IN 46206 $10.95/9 issues. Ages 5–13.

Children's Digest, Box 567B, Indianapolis, IN 46206 $10.95/9 issues. Ages 6–12.

Children's Playmate, Box 567B, Indianapolis, IN 46206 $13.95/9 issues. Ages 6–14.

Cobblestone, Box 959, Farmingdale, NY 11737 $16.50. History for young people. Articles, projects, puzzles. Excellent. Ages 6–18.

Cricket, Box 2672, Boulder, CO 80321 $15. Ages 6–12. Quality fiction.

Current Events, Xerox Educational Pub., 1250 Fairwood Ave., Columbus, OH 43216 $5.90/28 issues. For junior and senior high school students.

Current Science, Xerox Educational Pub., 1250 Fairwood Ave., Columbus, OH 43216 $5.90/28 issues. For junior and senior high school students.

Dynamite, Scholastic Home Periodicals, Box 1925, Marion, OH 43305 $10.95. Ages 8-12. Latest on super stars, magic, stories.

Ebony, Jr.!, 820 S. Michigan, Chicago, IL 60605 $8/10 issues. For black 6-12 year olds.

Electric Company Magazine, 200 Watt St., Box 2922, Boulder, CO 80322 $8.95/10 issues. Ages 6-10.

Highlights for Children, Box 269, Columbus, OH 43216 $39.95/33 issues (3 years). Ages 2-12.

Humpty Dumpty's, Box 567, Indianapolis, IN 46206 $10.95/9 issues. Ages 3-7.

Jack & Jill, Box 567, Indianapolis, IN 46206 $10.95/10 issues. Ages 5-12.

National Geographic World, Dept. 00482, 17th & M Streets N.W., Washington, DC 20036 $7.95. Ages 7 up. Wildlife, exotic places, interesting kids, posters.

Odyssey, Box 92788, Milwaukee, WI 53202 $15. Ages 6-12. "Young people's magazine of astronomy and outer space."

Owl, Scholastic Home Periodicals, Box 1925, Marion, OH 43305 $8.95/10 issues. All ages. Discoveries, animals, far-off places, famous people, projects.

Penny Power, Box 1906, Marion, OH 43302 $9/6 issues. Ages 6-16. Consumer Reports magazine for young people.

Ranger Rick's Nature Magazine, National Wildlife Federation, 8925 Leesburg Pike, Vienna, VA 22180 $10.50. Ages 4-14. Many photos, puzzles, articles.

Senior Scholastic, 2280 Arbor Blvd., Dayton, OH 45439 $5.75/18 issues. History, world report, government for senior high students.

Sesame Street Magazine, Box 2894, Boulder, CO 80322 $8.95/10 issues. Ages 2-6. Early learning games, cut-outs.

Seventeen, Radnor, PA 19088 $11.95

Sports & Athletes, 2120 Ave. of the Athletes, Box 1999, Marion, OH 43305 $13.50/9 issues

'Teen Magazine, Box 3297, Los Angeles, CA 90028 $11.95

Teen Word-Finds, 641 Lexington Ave., New York, NY 10022 $5.70/6 issues

3-2-1 Contact, E = MC Square, Box 2932, Boulder, CO 80321 $9.95/10 issues. Ages 8-14. Science discoveries, experiments, facts, puzzles, games.

Wee Wisdom, Unity Village, MO 64065 $4/10 issues. Ages 6-12.

Wow, Scholastic Home Periodicals, Box 1925, Marion, OH 43305 $8.95/9 issues. Ages 4-7. Pop-outs, records, books, posters with issues. Great fun.

Young Miss, 80 New Bridge Rd., Bergenfield, NJ 07621 $12/10 issues. Girls 10-14 years.

Your Big Backyard, National Wildlife Federation, 1412 16th St. N.W., Washington, DC 20036 $8.50. For the younger set.

Collectors

American Collector, Drawer C, Kermit, TX 79745 $8

Bottle News, Box 1000, Kermit, TX 79745 $7.50

Coin Prices, Iola, WI 54990 $8.50/6 issues

Coin World, 911 S. Vandemark Rd., Box 150, Sidney, OH 45367 $18/52 issues. Tabloid.

COINage, 17337 Ventura Blvd., Encino, CA 91316 $14

Coins, 700 E. State St., Iola, WI 54990 $13

Collectibles Illustrated, Depot Sq., Peterborough, NH 03458 $11.50

Hobbies, Magazine for Collectors, 1006 S. Michigan Ave., Chicago, IL 60605 $14

Jewelry Making Gems & Minerals, Box 687, Mentone, Ca 92359 $9.50

Linn's Stamp News, Box 29, Sidney, OH 45367 $17/52 issues. Tabloid.

Miniature Collector, 12 Queen Anne Place, Marion, OH 43302 $12/6 issues

Numismatic News, 700 E. State St., Iola, WI 54990 $16.50/52 issues. Tabloid.

The Numismatist, American Numismatic Association, Box 2366, Colorado Springs, CO 80901-2366 $15

Nutshell News, Clifton House, Clifton, VA 22024 $13/6 issues. "For complete miniatures hobbyist."

Rarities, 17337 Ventura Blvd., Encino, CA 91316 $10/6 issues. "Magazine of collectibles."

Sporting Classics, Box 770, Camden, SC 29020 $12. For collector of sporting and wildlife art, guns, books, decoys, etc.

Stamp World, Box 601, Sidney, OH 45367 $12

Stamps, 153 Waverly Place, New York, NY 10014 $13.80/52 issues.

World of Treasures, Box 253, Mt. Morris, IL 61054 $5/6 issues. Treasure hunting.

Computers

Creative Computing, Box 5214, Boulder, CO 80321 $24.97

Interface Age, 16704 Marquardt Ave., Cerritos, CA 90701 $18. "Computing for home and business."

Personal Computing, 4 Disk Dr., Box 1408, Riverton, NJ 08077 $18

Popular Computing, Box 307, Martinsville, NJ 08836 $15

Cooking

Bon Appetit, Box 2424, Boulder, CO 80302 $15

Cook's Magazine, The, 1698 Post Road E., Westport, CT 06880

Cuisine Magazine, Box 2640, Boulder, CO 80302 $14.97

Gourmet, Box 2980, Boulder, CO 80302 $18. Cooking, travel.

Crafts

American Craft, American Craft Council, 22 W. 55th St., New York, NY 10019 $25 (membership).

Ceramic Arts & Crafts, 30595 W. 8 Mile Rd., Livonia, MI 48152 $10

Ceramics Monthly, Box 12448, Columbus, OH 43212 $14

Crafts Magazine, 1 News Plaza, Marion, OH 43305 $15

Crafts 'N Things, 14 Main St., Park Ridge, IL 60068 $7/6 issues

Creative Crafts, Box 700, Newton, NJ 07860 $7/6 issues

Decorating & Craft Ideas, Box C-30, Birmingham, AL 35283 $12/10 issues

Glass Workshop, Box 244, Norwood, NJ 07648 $8/4 issues. Stained glass.

Handmade, 50 College St., Asheville, NC 28801 $14/4 issues

Lady's Circle Needlework, 23 West 26th St., New York, NY 10010 $9/4 issues

Needle & Thread, Box 10142, Des Moines, IA 50340 $12/6 issues

Pack-O-Fun, 14 Main St., Park Ridge, IL 60068 $4.95/4 issues. Scrapcraft.

Popular Ceramics, Box 6466, Glendale, CA 91205-0466 $14.76

Popular Handicraft, Box 428, Seabrook, NY 03874 $4/4 issues. "Hobbies for fun and profit."

Quilt World, Box 337, Seabrook, NY 03874 $3.50/2 issues

Rock & Gem, 17337 Ventura Blvd., Encino, CA 91316 $12

Stitch 'N Sew, Box 428, Seabrook, NY 03874 $6/6 issues. Quilts.

Workbasket, Box 5967, Kansas City, MO 64111 $4/10 issues

Cycling

Bicycle Motocross Action, Box 5277, Torrance, CA 90510 $4.50/6 issues

Bicycling, 33 East Minor St., Emmaus, PA 18049 $12.97

Bike World, 1400 Stierlin Rd., Mountain View, CA 94043 $7.50/7 issues

Cycle, Box 2776, Boulder, CO 80302 $13.98. Motorcyclists.

Cycle Guide, Box 267, Mt. Morris, IL 61054 $9.98. Motorcyclists.

Motocross Action, Box 317, Encino, CA 91316 $12.98

Touring Bike, 4247 E. La Palma Ave., Anaheim, CA. 92807 $13.95

Electronics, Audio, Video

Amateur Radio, CQ Magazine, 76 N. Broadway, Hicksville, NY 11801 $14

Audio, Box 5318, 1255 Portland Place, Boulder, CO 80322 $13.94.

Elementary Electronics, 380 Lexington Ave., New York, NY 10017 $6.95/ 6 issues

Ham Radio, Communications Technology, Greenville, NH 03048 $15

High Fidelity, Box 10759, Des Moines, IA 50340 $13.95.

High Technology, Box 2810, Boulder, CO 80322 $15

Hobby Radio, S9 Magazine, 14 Vanderventer Ave., Port Washington, NY 11050 $12

Popular Electronics, Box 2774, Boulder, CO 80302 $15

Radio Electronics, Box 2520, Boulder, CO 80322 $13

Stereo Review, Box 2771, Boulder, CO 80302 $9.98
Video, Box 1116, Dover, NJ 07801 $15. Home video.
Video Action, Box 255, Mt. Morris, IL 61054 $10
Video Review, Box 919, Farmingdale, NY 11737 $18. "Consumer video."
Videoplay, 51 Sugar Hollow Rd., Danbury, CT 06810 $6/6 issues. "How-to magazine for home video."

Games & Leisure

Bridge World, 39 W. 94th St., New York, NY 10025 $16
Chess Life, 186 Rt. 9W, New Windsor, NY 12550 $21. By U.S. Chess Federation.
Daytimers, 7060 Hollywood Blvd., Hollywood, CA 90028 $9.95. Soap opera news.
Electronic Games, Box 1128, Dover, NJ 07801 $15/6 issues
Games, Box 10145, Des Moines, IA 50340 $7.97/6 issues. Great fun.
Popular Bridge, 16001 Ventura Blvd., Encino, CA 91436 $7/6 issues
Soap Opera Digest, Box 2929, Boulder, CO 80302 $21/26 issues
Superb Word-Games, 641 Lexington Ave., New York, NY 10022 $7.50/6 issues
TV Guide, Box 900, Radnor, PA 19088 $23.40/52 issues

Gardening

Avant Gardener, Box 489, New York, NY 10028 $15/24 issues
Family Food Garden, 1999 Shepard Rd., St. Paul, MN 55116 $6/10 issues
Flower & Garden, 4251 Pennsylvania, Kansas City, MO 64111 $6. Northern, southern, western editions.
Gardener, 5560 Merle Hay Rd., Des Moines, IA 50323 $5/6 issues. For men gardeners.
Herb Grower Magazine, Falls Village, CT 06031 $6/4 issues
Organic Gardening, 33 E. Minor St., Emmaus, PA 18049 $11
Under Glass, Lord & Burnham, Box 114, Irvington, NY 10533 $2.75/6 issues. Greenhouse gardening.

General Interest

Business Week, Box 506, Hightstown, NJ 08520 $34.95/52 issues
Changing Times, Editors Park, MD 20782 $15. Economic and family subjects.
Christian Herald, Box 371, Chappaqua, NY 10514 $11.97/11 issues
Ebony, 820 S. Michigan Ave., Chicago, IL 60605 $16. For Black readers.
Forbes, 60 5th Ave., New York, NY 10114 $33/26 issues
Fortune, Time-Life Bldg., Chicago, IL 60611 $33
Good Old Days, Box 428, Seabrook, NH 03874 $7. Nostalgia.
Grit, 208 W. 3rd St., Williamsport, PA 17701 $13.50/52 issues. "America's family newspaper."
Life, 541 N. Fairbanks Ct., Chicago, IL 60611 $19.95

Money, Box 2518, Boulder, CO 80322 $21.95
Mother Earth News, Box 70, Hendersonville, NC 28791 $18/6 issues
National Geographic, Box 2895, Washington, DC 20013 $20.25/18 issues
National Review, 150 E. 35th St., New York, NY 10016 $26/26 issues
Newsweek, Newsweek Bldg., Box 403, Livingston, NJ 07039 $39/52 issues
People Weekly, Time-Life Bldg., Chicago, IL 60611 $39/52 issues
Psychology Today, Box 2990, Boulder, CO 80302 $13.97
Reader's Digest, Pleasantville, NY 10570 $12.93
Reader's Digest, Large-Type Edition, Reader's Digest Fund for the Blind, Inc.,
   Pleasantville, NY 10570 $10.95
Saturday Evening Post, Box 3400, Bergenfield, NJ 07621 $12/9 issues
Smithsonian, Box 2955, Boulder, CO 80322 $17. History, art, ideas, science.
Time, Time-Life Bldg., Chicago, IL 60611 $40/52 issues
Us, Box 10193, Des Moines, IA 50340 $17.95/26 issues. Celebrities.
U.S. News & World Report, Box 2627, Boulder, CO 80321 $31/52 issues

Good Reading

The Atlantic Monthly, Box 2547, Boulder, CO 80322 $18
Book Digest, Box 2451, Boulder, CO 80302 $14
Harper's, 1255 Portland Place, Boulder, CO 80323 $18
International Short Story Magazine, Box 405, Great Neck, NY 11022 $15/
   6 issues. Tales by the world's leading contemporary writers.
New Yorker, 25 W. 43rd St., New York, NY 10036 $28/weekly

Gracious Living

Americana, 381 West Center St., Marion, OH 43302 $11.90/6 issues. Dec-
   orating, antiques, travel, horticulture, exhibits, etc.
Architectural Digest, Box 2415, Boulder, CO 80322 $36
Better Homes and Gardens, Box 4536, Des Moines, IA 50336 $12
Connoisseur, Box 10120, Des Moines, IA 50350 $19.95. Archeology, travel,
   art, etc.
Home, Box 10050, Des Moines, IA 50340 $15. Design.
House and Garden, Box 5202, Boulder, CO 80322 $12
House Beautiful, Box 10083, Des Moines, IA 50350 $13.97
Metropolitan Home, 1716 Locust St., Des Moines, IA 50336 $12
Southern Living, Box C-119, Birmingham, AL 35283 $17.95

Handyman

Family Handyman, 52 Woodhaven Rd., Marion, OH 44302 $9.95/10 issues
Home Energy Digest, 8009 34th Ave. South, Minneapolis, MN 55420 $12.95/
   4 issues.
Homeowners How-To, Box 2842, Boulder, CO 80322 $11.94/6 issues
Mechanix Illustrated, Box 2830, Boulder, CO 80322 $11.94

New Shelter, Emmaus, PA 18049 $10. Solar and other new energy-saving ideas plus old ones revived.

Popular Mechanics, Box 10064, Des Moines, IA 50350 $9.97

Workbench, Box 5967, Kansas City, MO 64111 $6/6 issues

Health & Fitness

American Health, Box 10035, Des Moines, IA 50340 $12/6 issues. "Fitness of body and mind."

Chimo, 18 Duncan St., Toronto, Ontario M5H 3G8 Canada $17.50. Holistic.

Health, Box 3700, Bergenfield, NJ 07621 $15

Health Express, 7422 Mountjoy Dr., Huntington Beach, CA 92648 $18. By International Academy of Nutritional Consultants.

Prevention, 33 E. Minor St., Emmaus, PA 18049 $10.97

Shape, 21100 Erwin St., Woodland Hills, CA 91367 $20

Slimmer, Box 28877, San Diego, CA 92128 $10/6 issues

Weight Watchers Magazine, Box 2555, Boulder, CO 80302 $9.97

Hearing Impaired

Deaf American, National Association of the Deaf, 814 Thayer Ave., Silver Spring, MD 20910 $6/11 issues

History

American Heritage, Box 977, Farmingdale, NY 11737 $24/6 issues

American History Illustrated, National Historical Society, Box 1776, Marion, OH 43302 $16.95/10 issues

American West, Box 1960, Marion, OH 43305 $15/6 issues

Mankind, 8060 Melrose Ave., Los Angeles, CA 90046 $6/4 issues. "Magazine of popular history."

Old West, Iola, WI 54990 $4.95/6 issues

True West, Iola, WI 54990 $8.95

Horses

American Cowboy, Box 311, Walsenburg, CO 81089 $10/6 issues. Rodeo.

Appaloosa News, Box 8403, Moscow, ID 83843 $7.50

Classic, 551 5th Ave., New York, NY 10017 $15. About horses and sport.

Horse & Horseman, Box HH, Capistrano Beach, CA 92624 $14

Horse & Rider, Box 555, Temecula, CA 92390 $12

Horse Illustrated, Box 4120, San Clemente, CA 92672 $12.95/12 issues (2 years)

Horseman, Box 10973, Houston, TX 77292-0973 $15

Western Horse Magazine, Box 636, Sun City, CA 92381 $15

Western Horseman, Box 7980, Colorado Springs, CO 80933 $12

Lifestyle

Christian Life, Box 305, Dover, NJ 07801 $12.95
50 Plus, 99 Garden St., Marion, OH 43302 $15 "How to plan for the quality years. How to enjoy them."
Gifted Children Newsletter, Box 115, Sewell, NJ 08080 $24
Intro, Box INTRO, Studio City, CA 91604 $15. Singles.
Mother's Manual, 420 Lexington Ave., New York, NY 10017 $3/6 issues
Parents Magazine, Box 7000, Bergenfield, NJ 07621 $12

Men

Esquire, Box 2590, Boulder, CO 80321 $15.94
Gentleman's Quarterly, Box 2962, Boulder, CO 80322 $18
Playboy, Box 2420, Boulder, CO 80302 $18

Model Building

Flying Models, Box 700, Newton, NJ 07860 $15
Military Modeler, 10968 Via Frontera, San Diego, CA 92127 $22.50
Model Airplane News, with *R/C Boats & Cars,* 837 Post Rd., Darien, CT 06820 $20
Model Builder, 621 W. 19th St., Box 335, Costa Mesa, CA 92627-0132 $25
Model Railroader, 1027 N. 7th St., Milwaukee, WI 53233 $20
Rail Classics, 10968 Via Frontera, San Diego, CA 92127 $11.50/6 issues
Railfan & Railroad, Box 700, Newton, NJ 07860 $8/6 issues
Railroad Model Craftsman, Box 700, Newton, NJ 07860 $16
RC Modeler, Box 487, Sierra Madre, CA 91024 $24. Radio control enthusiasts.
Scale Modeler, 10968 Via Frontera, San Diego, CA 92127 $22.50
Scale R/C Modeler, 10968 Via Frontera, San Diego, CA 92127 $11.50/6 issues
Scale Ship Modeler, 10968 Via Frontera, San Diego, CA 92127 $13.50/6 issues
Trains, The Magazine of Railroading, 1027 N. 7th St., Milwaukee, WI 53233 $20

Music

Country Music, Box 5300, Bergenfield, NJ 07621 $12/10 issues
Country Rhythms, 475 Park Ave. South, New York, NY 10016 $19.98
Country Song Roundup, Charlton Bldg., Derby, CT 06418 $12.50
Down Beat, 222 W. Adams St., Chicago, IL 60606 $13.50. Contemporary music.
Frets, Box 28836, San Diego, CA 92128 $17.95. Acoustic string instruments.
Guitar Player, Box 28836, San Diego, CA 92128 $17.95
Guitar Review, 409 E. 50th St., New York, NY 10022 $16/3 issues. Classic guitar.
Guitar World, 79 Madison Ave., New York, NY 10016 $21

High Fidelity/Musical America, Box 10765, Des Moines, IA 50340 $24
Hit Parader, Charlton Bldg., Derby, CT 06418 $9/6 issues
Instrumentalist, 1418 Lake St., Evanston, IL 60204 $14.50. Serious musicians.
International Musician & Recording World, GPO Box 2367, New York, NY
    10116 $21
Keyboard, Box 28836, San Diego, CA 92128 $17.95
Modern Drummer, 1000 Clifton Ave., Clifton, NJ 07013 $15.95/9 issues
Music & Sound Output, 220 Westbury Ave., Carle Place, NY 11514 $12/
    6 issues
Music Exchange, Box 6, Atwood, CA 92601 $10/6 issues. "How-to magazine
    of music success."
Musician, Box 989, Farmingdale, NY 11737 $18
Opera News, 1865 Broadway, New York, NY 10023 $30 (includes membership
    in Metropolitan Opera Guild).
Record Review, Box 91878, Los Angeles, CA 90009 $9/6 issues
Sing Out!, 505 8th St., New York, NY 10018 $11/6 issues. Folk songs.

Outdoors

Adventure Travel, Box 10028, Des Moines, IA 50348 $15
American Hunter, 1600 Rhode Island Ave. N.W., Washington, DC 20036
    $15. By National Rifle Association.
American Rifleman, 1600 Rhode Island Ave. N.W., Washington, DC. 20036
    $15. By National Rifle Association.
Archery, Rt. 2, Box 514, Redlands, CA 92373 $5. Hunting, fishing.
Archery World, 225 E. Michigan, Milwaukee, WI 53202 $9/6 issues
Backpacker, Box 2784, Boulder, CO 80321 $16/6 issues
Bow & Arrow, Box HH, Capistrano Beach, CA 92624 $9/6 issues
Bowhunter, 3808 S. Calhoun St., Fort Wayne, IN 46807 $9/6 issues
Camping Journal, Box 2620, Greenwich, CT 06835 $7.95/8 issues
Climbing, Box E, Aspen, CO 81611 $7.50/6 issues
Country Gentleman, Box 4900, Bergenfield, NJ 07621 $6/4 issues. "Coun-
    try living."
Field & Stream, 1255 Portland Place, Box 2824, Boulder, CO 80321 $7.95
Fishing & Hunting News, Box C 19000, Seattle, WA 98109 $15/52 issues.
    Regional editions.
Fishing Facts, Box 609, Menomonee Falls, WI 53051 $17.88
Fishing World, 51 Atlantic Ave., Floral Park, NY 11001 $4/6 issues
Fly-Fisherman, Box 2705, Boulder, CO 80231 $11.97/7 issues
Fur-Fish-Game, 2878 E. Main St., Columbus, OH 43209 $6
Gun World, Box HH, Capistrano Beach, CA 92624 $14
Guns & Ammo, Box 3292, Los Angeles, CA 90028 $11.94
Guns Magazine, Suite 200, 591 Camino Reina, San Diego, CA 92108 $14.95
In-Fisherman, Box 999, Brainerd, MN 56401-0999 $15/6 issues. Fresh water
    fishing.
Off Belay, The Mountain Magazine, 15630 S.E. 124th St., Renton, WA 98055
    $9/6 issues

Outdoor Life, Boulder, CO 80301 $13.94

Outside, Box 2690, Boulder, CO 80321 $9/8 issues. Sports, travel, energy, news, science.

Petersen's Hunting Magazine, Box 3353, Los Angeles, CA 90028 $11.94

ProBass, 15115 S. 76th E. Ave., Bixby, OK 74008 $10/6 issues

Salmon Trout Steelheader, Box 02112, Portland, OR 97202 $6.95/6 issues

Salt Water Sportsman, Box 6050, Marion, OH 43302 $15

Shooting Times, 357 Magnum Blvd., Marion, OH 43302 $13.95

Sierra Club Magazine, Box 7959, San Francisco, CA 94120 $3/6 issues

Southern Outdoors, Box 17915, Montgomery, AL 36141 $9.95

Sports Afield, Box 10069, Des Moines, IA 50350 $11.97

Summit, 44 Mill Creek Rd., Big Bear Lake, CA 92315 $8/6 issues. Mountaineering.

Wilderness Camping, 1597 Union St., Schenectady, NY 12309 $5.90/6 issues

Photography

American Cinematographer, P.O. Box 2230, Hollywood, CA 90028

American Photographer, Box 2833, Boulder, CO 80302 $17.90

Camera Arts, Box 2783, Boulder, CO 80302 $18/6 issues

Camera 35, GPO Box 1812, New York, NY 10116 $20

Modern Photography, Box 10786, Des Moines, IA 50340 $15.95

Petersen's Photographic Magazine, 6725 Sunset Blvd., Los Angeles, CA 90028

Popular Photography, Box 2775, Boulder, CO 80302 $11.97

Running

Runner, The, Box 2730, Boulder, CO 80302 $15

Runner's World, Box 366, Mountain View, CA 94042 $14.95

Running, Box 350, Mt. Morris, IL 61054 $9.95/6 issues

Running Times, 12808 Occoquan Rd., Woodbridge, VA 22192 $15

Science

Asimov's Science Fiction Magazine, Box 1933, Marion, OH 43305 $19.50/ 13 issues

Astronomy, Box 92788, Milwaukee, WI 53202 $15

Discover, Time-Life Bldg., 541 N. Fairbanks Ct., Chicago, IL 60611 $19.95. Archaeology, psychology, technology, etc. "Newsmagazine of science."

Futurist, 4916 St. Elmo Ave., Washington, DC 20014 $18/6 issues. Forecasts, trends and ideas about the future.

Mineralogical Record, Box 35565, Tucson, AZ 85740 $20/6 issues

Natural History, American Museum of Natural History, Box 4300, Bergenfield, NJ 07621 $15

Omni, Box 908, Farmingdale, NY 11735 $24. Astronomy, arts, fiction, behavior, biomedicine, etc.

Popular Science, Box 2881, Boulder, CO 80321 $13.94

Science, American Association for Advancement of Science, 1515 Massachusetts Ave. N.W., Washington, DC 20005 $48/52 issues. Research, news, products.

Science Digest, Box 10076, Des Moines, IA 50350 $11.97/10 issues

Science 82, Box 10778, Des Moines, IA 50347 $15/10 issues. Varied disciplines of technology, biochemistry, wildlife, sports, etc.

The Sciences, 2 E. 63rd St., New York, NY 10021 $12.50/10 issues. By New York Academy of Sciences.

Scientific American, Box 5919, New York, NY 10164 $21. Scholarly science.

Sky & Telescope, 49 Bay State Rd., Cambridge, MA 02238-1290 $15

Space World, 318 Main St., Amherst, Wis. 54406 $14/10 issues

Technology Illustrated, Box 2806, Boulder, CO 80322 $10/6 issues. Medicine, computers, etc.

Snow Sports

Nordic Skiing, Box 106, West Brattleboro, VT 05301 $10.95/7 issues. Cross-country skiers.

Powder, Box 1028, Dana Point, CA 92629 $9.95/7 issues. Snow skiing.

Ski, Box 2795, Boulder, CO 80302 $13.94/7 issues

Skier's World, Box 2683, 1255 Portland Place, Boulder, CO 80322 $10/7 issues

Skiing, Box 2777, Boulder, CO 80302 $9.98

Snowgoer, 1999 Shepard Rd., St. Paul MN 55116 $6.25/5 issues

Sports

See *Magazines: Snow Sports, Water Sports, Outdoors.*

Baseball Digest, Box 5031, Des Moines, IA 50340 $11.95

Basketball Digest, Box 4582, Des Moines, IA 50340 $7.95/8 issues

Black Belt Magazine, 1813 Victory Place, Burbank, CA 91504 $21

Bowling Magazine, 5301 S. 76th St., Greendale, WI 53929 $4

Football Digest, Box 4593, Des Moines, IA 50340 $9.95/10 issues

Goal, Box 999, Ridgefield, NJ 07657 $12.25/7 issues. National Hockey League magazine.

Golf, 380 Madison Ave., New York, NY 10017 $7.95

Golf Digest, Box 10180, Des Moines, IA 50340 $14.95

Golf Magazine, Box 2786, Boulder, CO 80302 $11.94

Golf World, Box 2000, Southern Pines, NC 28387 $16.50/52 issues

Hockey Digest, Box 4595, Des Moines, IA 50340 $7.95/8 issues

Inside Kung-Fu, Box 161, Mt. Morris, IL 61054 $18.75

Inside Sports, Box 2559, Boulder, CO 80322 $18

International Gymnast, 410 Broadway, Box 110, Santa Monica, CA 90406 $18

Kick Illustrated, Box 173, Mt. Morris, IL 61054 $16.75. Martial arts.

Pro!, Box 939, Farmingdale, NY 11737 $18/7 issues

Pro Football Monthly, Box 239, Palisades, NY 10964 $20

Racquetball Illustrated, Box 261, Mt. Morris, IL 61054 $16.75

Ring, 120 W. 31st St., New York, NY 10001 $15. International boxing.
Skating Magazine, 20 1st St., Colorado Springs, CO 80906 $7.50/10 issues. Figure skating.
Soccer America, Box 23704, Oakland, CA 94623 $23/50 issues
Soccer Digest, Box 10170, Des Moines, IA 50340 $5.95/6 issues
Sport, Box 5016, Des Moines, IA 50306 $12
Sporting News, 100 Stadium Dr., Marion, OH 43305 $36/52 issues
Sports Illustrated, 541 N. Fairbanks Ct., Chicago, IL 60611 $36/52 issues
Super Sports, 235 Park Ave. South, New York, NY 10003 $6/4 issues
Tennis USA, Chilton Way, Radnor, PA 19089 $7
Track & Field News, Box 10281, Palo Alto, CA 94303 $15.50
Women's Sports, 331 Town & Country Village, Palo Alto, CA 94301 $10
World Tennis, Box 5341, Boulder, CO 80322 $15.94
Yoga Journal, 2054 University Ave. #607, Berkeley, CA 94704 $11/6 issues

Travel

Black Odyssey, 114 E. 28th St., Rm 700, New York, NY 11434 $15. Black travel and leisure ideas.
Cruise Travel, Box 10139, Des Moines, IA 50340 $12/6 issues
Going Places, 1400 W. Greenleaf, Chicago, IL 60626 $12/6 issues.
Motor Home, Box 2735, Boulder, CO 80302 $14.90/9 issues
Parks & Recreation, National Recreation & Park Association, 3101 Park Center Dr., Alexandria, VA 22302 $12
Trailer Life, Box 2739, Boulder, CO 80322 $11.94
Travel & Leisure, Box 777, Great Neck, NY 11025 $18
Travel/Holiday, Travel Bldg., Floral Park, NY 11001 $9

Water Sports

Skin Diver, Box 3295, Los Angeles, CA 90028 $11.94
Surfer, Box 1028, Dana Point, CA 92629 $15
Surfing, Box 28816, San Diego, CA 92128 $15
Swim, Swim, Box 5901, Santa Monica, CA 90405 $10/6 issues.
Water Ski, Box 4779, Winter Park, FL 32793 $16/10 issues
Wind Rider, Box 183, Mt. Morris, IL 61054 $9.95/6 issues. Boardsailing.
Wind Surf, Box 561, Dana Point, CA 92629 $12/6 issues
World Waterskiing Magazine, Box 136, Mt. Morris, IL 61054 $9.95/7 issues

Women

Cosmopolitan, Box 10074, Des Moines, IA 50340 $24
Elan, Box 2904, Boulder, CO 80322 $11.95/6 issues. "Multidimensional living, career management, fashion and culture."
Essence, Box 2989, Boulder, CO 80321 $8.96. For Black women.
Every Woman, Box 222, Mt. Morris, IL 61054 $23.40/12 issues (2 years)

Family Circle, 488 Madison Ave., New York, NY 10017 $11.97/17 issues
Glamour, Box 5203, Boulder, CO 80322 $12
Good Housekeeping, Box 10055, Des Moines, IA 50374 $12.97
Harper's Bazaar, Box 10081, Des Moines, IA 50350 $14.97
Ladies Home Journal, Box 1697, Des Moines, IA 50340 $11.97
Lady's Circle, 23 W. 26th St., New York, NY 10010 $18
Mademoiselle, Box 5204, Boulder, CO 80322 $12
McCall's, Box 10293, Des Moines, IA 50336 $11.95
Ms., 123 Garden St., Marion, OH 43302 $12
New Woman, P.O. Drawer 189, Palm Beach, FL 33480 $15
Redbook, Box 5242, Des Moines, IA 50340 $11.97
Savvy, Box 2495, Boulder, CO 80322 $12
Self, Box 5216, Boulder, CO 80322 $12
Vogue, Box 5201, Boulder, CO 80302 $24
Woman's Day, I.F.S., Box 807, Mineola, NY 11501. Foreign subscriptions
    only. $23.70. U.S. military (overseas), $11.85
Women's Circle, Box 428, Seabrook, NH 03874 $7
Working Mother, Box 10609, Des Moines, IA 50336 $9.95/6 issues
Working Woman, Box 10132, Des Moines, IA 50340 $16

Writing

Writer, 8 Arlington St., Boston, MA 02116 $15
Writer's Digest, 205 W. Center St., Marion, OH 43305 $18

Catalogs

Now you know what gift you want to buy—but do you know where to find it? Maybe a mail-order catalog will have the answer.

Order several catalogs in a merchandise category that interests you so that you can compare prices and styles. It doesn't hurt to compare local prices, too, since catalogs do not always offer savings. (Be sure to add shipping costs to the catalog prices.) However, some will contain good bargains, additional gift ideas, and a lot of enjoyable reading.

You can request the free catalogs with a post card. When money is required, send it by check. Remember that prices will change and some companies may discontinue their catalogs.

To be safe, request a catalog four months before you need a gift. That allows two months for delivery of the catalog, another two months for your merchandise to arrive. Most firms reply within two weeks, but there are some slow-pokes and sometimes merchandise has to be back-ordered. All Christmas orders should be mailed by November 1 to be reasonably sure of their arriving on time. Order even earlier if you will be mailing the gift.

Check the return policy on goods before you order. Most catalog companies will let you return products in thirty days, but a few will not accept returns unless they are defective. If you give your gift more than thirty days after you have received it and then have to return it, write the firm explaining the circumstances. More than likely, they will allow its return.

A listing of a catalog company here does not mean I endorse or recommend it. I have found mail order, on the whole, to be a pleasant way of shopping, but have not had personal experience with many of these firms.

Animals, Animal Lovers, Birds & Fish	Food	Models & Miniatures
Art & Special Treasures	Gardening	Movies
Audio	Handcrafts	Music
Aviation	Handicapped	Outdoors & Sports
Boating	Handyman	Photography
Books	Health & Beauty	Science
Clothing	Hearing Impaired	Smorgasbord
Collectors	Home Furnishings	Stationery
Craft Supplies	Housewares	Toys & Games
Cycling	Indian Supplies (crafts)	Typewriter
Electronics	International Goods	Visually Impaired
	Jewelry	Western
	Lefties	

Animals, Animal Lovers, Birds & Fish

A.I. Root Co., Box 706, Medina, OH 44256. Free, 32p. Bee keeping supplies.

Animal Veterinary Products, Box 1267, Galesburg, IL 61401. Free, 130p. Thorough assortment of supplies, books, food supplements, grooming aids.

Audubon Workshop, 1501 Paddock Dr., Northbrook, IL 60062. Free, 48p. Bird baths, feeders, houses; housewares of all kinds with birds on them.

Duncraft, 25 S. Main St., Penacook, NH 03303. Free, 32p. Feeders, seed for wild birds; books, etc.

Du-Say's, 301 S. Curran St., Picayune, MS 39466. Free, 32p. "Everything for the pampered pet"—doggie coats to scratching posts.

Echo Products, 335 Mills St., Ortonville, MI 48462. 50 cents, 24p. Everything for the aquarium including the fish.

Katnip Tree Co., Box 9594, Seattle, WA 98109. 25 cents, 16p. Cat toys, cages, catnip tree, etc.

Kester's Wild Game Food Nurseries, Inc. (See *Catalogs: Gardening*)

Petco Animal Supplies, Box 1076, La Mesa, CA 92041-9984. Free, 112p. Supplies for birds, aquariums, horses, dogs, cats.

Satra's Purr Palace, Rt. 1, Box 175, Elkhorn, WI 53121. $1, 12p. Items for cats, cat lovers.

Schenker Animal Reproductions, 431 Plandome Rd., Manhasset, NY 11030. Over 80 breeds of dogs, cats, horses reproduced on ties, handbags, mugs, stationery and lots of other items.

Sporting Dog Specialties, Box 68, Spencerport, NY 14559. Free, 32p. Art prints, training aids, supplies, books, and gift items with dog or sporting motif.

Wild Bird Specialties, 4815 Oak St., Crystal Lake, IL 60014. Free, 32p. Bird feeders, seed, houses, books.

Wildlife Nurseries (see *Catalogs: Gardening*).

Art & Special Treasures

Aladdin House Ltd., 654 Ninth Ave., New York, NY 10036. Brochures, $3/year. Artifacts, antiquities, reproductions from ancient times.

American Museum of Natural History, Museum Shop Catalog, Box 174, Scarsdale, NY 10583. 50 cents, 20p. Exquisite jewelry and gift items from museum's collections: Japanese porcelain vase, Chinese embroidered stole, Carvajales ceramic animals, etc.

Associated American Artists, 663 Fifth Ave., New York, NY 10022. 50 cents, 52p. Original art prints, etchings, lithographs, serigraphs, woodcuts. Signed, limited editions.

Bijan, 14123 Oxnard St., Van Nuys, CA 91401. Free, 12p. Brass and marble sculpture.

Brooklyn Museum Gallery Shop, Eastern Pkwy., Brooklyn, NY 11238. Free, 22p. Exotic art work, jewelry, decorator items.

Colonial Williamsburg, P.O. Box CH, Williamsburg, VA 23187. Free, 20p. Reproductions of jewelry, housewares, decorative items from 18th and early 19th century. Also Craft House catalog, 285p., $8.95. Over 2,000 reproductions of furniture, textiles, wallpaper, tableware, etc.

Corrigan's, 923 Main St., Houston, TX 77002. Free, several catalogs throughout the year. Elegant jewelry, crystal, silver, porcelain, other fine gifts.

Freer Gallery of Art, Smithsonian Institution, Washington, DC 20560. Free, 72p. Prints, desk accessories, needlework kits, greeting cards and notepaper, jewelry and gift selections with Oriental flavor.

Glassmasters, 27 W. 23rd St., New York, NY 10010. $1, 20p. Nature, gnomes, and other lovely designs in vitric enamel on glass. Window hangings.

Metropolitan Museum of Art, Box 255, Gracie Station, New York, NY 10028. Free, 48p. $1, 116p. Reproductions, prints, scarves, note paper, books, jewelry, porcelain dinnerware, etc.

Museum of Modern Art, Customer Sales Service, 11 W. 53rd St., New York, NY 10019. $1, 20p. Interesting paper goods, art prints, books, serving items, games.

National Trust for Historic Preservation, 1600 H Street N.W., Washington, DC 20006. $1, 24p. Exquisite reproductions of decorative accessories, sterling jewelry, toys, collector's items from their historic properties.

Smithsonian Catalogue, Smithsonian Institution, Box 2456, Washington, DC 20013. Free, 40p. Unique assortment of toys, gifts, serving pieces, jewelry, etc. of collector quality.

Steuben Glass, 5th Ave. at 56th St., New York, NY 10022. $4, 224p. book. Fine crystal animals, prismatics, vases, glassware, paper weights, etc. Extraordinary and expensive.

Audio

(See *Catalogs: Music*).

Audio Accessories Co., 38W515 Deerpath Rd., Batavia, IL 60510. Free price list. Children's stories on audio cassettes.

Books on Tape, Box 7900, Newport Beach, CA 92660. Free, 130p. Rent or buy cassette tapes of mysteries, classics, history, children's stories, more.

Caedmon, 1995 Broadway, New York, NY 10023. Free, 48p. Over 1000 spoken word and classical music cassettes and records. Shakespeare, modern plays, humor, children's entertainment, etc.

House of Tyrol, Box 909, Gateway Plaza, Cleveland, GA 30528. $1, 32p. LPs, 8-track, cassettes. Popular and folk music from around the world.

Record Hunter, 507 5th Ave., New York, NY 10017. Free, 12p. LPs, cassettes, 8-track cartridges at good discounts.

Rose Records, 214 S. Wabash Ave., Chicago, IL 60604. Free, 12p. LPs and cassettes of classics, current hits, children's stories, gospel, etc.

Saxitone Tape Sales, 1776 Columbia Rd. N.W., Washington, DC 20009-2896. Free, 32p. All kinds of audio equipment and blank cassette tapes.

Thomas J. Valentino, 151 W. 46th St., New York, NY 10036. Free, 150p. Almost any sound effect on tape, magnetic film transfers, 16mm, 35mm.

Aviation

Aero Publishers, 329 W. Aviation Rd., Fallbrook, CA 92028. Free, 34p. Aviation humor, history, guides.

The Cockpit, 627 Broadway, New York, NY 10012. $1, 32p. Flight jackets, WWII memorabilia; military, special unit and flight insignia and patches; other aviation gear and gifts.

Sporty's Pilot Shop, Clermont County Airport, Batavia, OH 45103-9988. Free, 70p. Assorted aviation supplies, books, jewelry, gifts.

Wag-Aero, Box 181, 1216 North Rd., Lyons, WI 53148. Free, 90p. Tools and parts for the home aircraft builder.

Boating

Commodore Nautical Supplies, 396 Broadway, New York, NY 10013. $1, 108p. Clothing, nautical accessories, galley supplies, jewelry, linens, dishware, etc.

Defender Industries Inc., Box 820, New Rochelle, NY 10801. $1, 168p. Marine Buyers' Guide. Hardware, resins, essential instruments for bigger boats, yachts.

E&B Marine Supply, 150 Jackson Ave., Edison, NJ 08818. Free, 120p. Over 3500 items for power and sailboats—clothing, hardware, galley equipment, pumps, etc.

Folbot Corp, Box 7097, Charleston, SC 29405. Free, 50p. Kayaks and small craft that fold up.

Goldbergs' Marine, 202 Market St., Philadelphia, PA 19106. $2, 228p. Depth finders to deck chairs.

Hans Klepper Corp., 35 Union Square West, New York, NY 10003. Free, 8p. Folding boats, kayaks; accessories.

International Marine Publishing Co., 21 Elm St., Camden, ME 04843. Free, 16p. Almost any subject for boat lovers—boatbuilding, racing, sport fishing, maritime history, modeling, sea tales, etc.

James Bliss, Rt. 128 at Exit 61, Dedham, MA 02026. Free, 268pp. Aimed at yachtsmen. Basics plus galley items, clothing.

Lands' End, 105 Leffler St., Dodgeville, WI 53533. Free, 48p. Canvas luggage, clothing, boating accessories.

Leisure Imports, 104 Arlington Ave., St. James, NY 11780. Free, 8p. Inflatable canoes, dinghies, accessories; sun couch.

Peabody Museum of Salem, East India Square, Salem, MA 01970. Free publications list. 50 cents, 24p. catalog. Maritime prints, plates, books.

Preston's, 102 S. Main St. Wharf, Greenport, NY 11944. 25 cents, 128p. Ship models; nautical brassware, housewares, gifts; marine pictures; figureheads; ship's lights, clocks.

Ship Shop, 1 Larkfield Rd., E. Northport, NY 11731. Free, 80p. Boat hardware, cabin accessories, clothing, instruments.

Wind in the Rigging, 125 E. Main St., Port Washington, WI 53074. Free, 12 p. Nautical clothing, jewelry, belts and other gift items.

Books

Aspen Cabin, Box 1509, Durango, CO 81301. Free, 14p. Fascinating collection of wilderness books: survival, hunting, energy, skills, prospecting.

Bantam Books, 666 Fifth Ave., New York, NY 10103. Free, 36p. Over 1600 titles from finance to romance.

Bellerophon Books, 36 Anacapa St., Santa Barbara, CA 93101. Free, 8p. Wonderful posters to color, coloring books, books, cut-outs for children. Ancient times, Shakespeare, space, dance, dinosaurs, many more intriguing subjects. Most under $3.

Books on Tape. See *Gift Ideas: Visually Impaired.*

Classic Motorbooks, Box 1, Osceola, WI 54020. $2, 120p. Amazing array of titles on racing, history, motorcycles, repairs, trucks, military, investment in cars, etc.

Dover Publications, 180 Varick St., New York, NY 10014. Free, 138p. Books in many fields—art, children's, etc.

Edward R. Hamilton Bookseller, 98 Clapboard Ridge Rd., Danbury, CT 06810. Free, 20p. Publishers' overstocks, returns at prices well below retail. All new books.

Emerson Books, Madelyn Ave., Verplanck, NY 10596. Free, 32p. How-to books on many subjects from card tricks to yoga.

Garden Way Publishing Co., Charlotte, VT 05445. Free catalog, fliers. Books on gardening, farm living, energy alternatives, country skills.

Goodspeed's Book Shop, 7 Beacon St., Boston, MA 02108. $3, 130p. Over 4500 books on individual genealogies, local histories, colonial and revolutionary records, peerage, English local histories.

Hacker Art Books, 54 W. 57th St., New York, NY 10019. Free, 16p. Books from U.S. and Europe on fine and applied art, architecture, and archaeology; also collectors' books.

Harvey House, 128 W. River St., Chippewa Falls, WI 54729. Free, 24p. Variety of books for children and youth.

Hotchkiss House, 18 Hearthstone Rd., Pittsford, NY 14534. Free, 8p. Over 800 titles on 50 categories of antiques, arts, hobbies, and collectibles.

Lamplighter Books, Leon, IA 50144. Free, 4pp. Books on all kinds of crafts, hobbies, collectibles, antiques.

Library of Congress, Central Service Division, Washington, DC 20540. Free, 72pp. "Publications in Print." Over 500 books, pamphlets, and serials on varied subjects, many historical; also folk records and literary recordings.

Owen Davies Bookseller, 200 W. Harrison St., Oak Park, IL 60304. Free, 24p. Books about aviation, railroads, ships around the world.

Publishers Central Bureau, 1 Champion Ave., Avenel, NJ 07131. Free. Books, records—many at big savings.

Rodale Press, 33 E. Minor St., Emmaus, PA 18049. Free, 56p. Books on cooking, gardening, energy saving, health, nutrition, bicycling.

Sanshar Crafts, Box 82, Homecrest Station, Brooklyn, NY 11229. Free. Craft supplies. 9p. of craft books.

Unicorn, Box 645, Rockville, MD 20851. $1, 24p. Hobby, craft books.

Clothing

Family

Baker Street Collection, 281 Centennial Ave., Piscataway, NJ 08854. Free, 16p. 30 classic shirt styles.

Brooks Bros., 346 Madison Ave., New York, NY 10017. Free, 48p. Mostly men's clothing (pajamas to suits) in cotton blends; some women's separates.

Deerskin Trading Post, 119 Foster St., Peabody, MA 01960. Free, 32p. Leather, suede coats, shoes, jackets, hats, handbags, gloves; men's and women's.

Dunham's of Maine, Waterville, ME 04901. Free, 32p. Fine, classic clothing for men and women; some accessories.

Lew Magram, 830 7th Ave., New York, NY 10019. $1, 36p. Name designer clothes and accessories, mostly for men.

Norm Thompson, Box 3999, Portland, OR 97208. Free, 88p. Mostly casual clothing, many European imports.

Talbots, 175 Beal St., Hingham, MA 02043. Free, 74p. Classic styling, mostly casual women's and men's clothing.

Men

Cable Car Clothiers, c/o Robert Kirk, Ltd., No. 150, Post St., San Francisco, CA 94108. Free, 64p. British made suits, shirts, slacks, hats, and accessories for men. Some women's clothing.

Hitchcock, 165 Beal St., Hingham, MA 02043. Free, several through year. Wide shoes for men. Over 100 styles. EE through EEEEEE.

Women

Avon Fashions, Avon Lane, Newport News, VA 23630. Free, 64p. Youthful fashions, mostly casual.

Bedford Fair, 157 Kisco Ave., Mt. Kisco, NY 10549. Free, 32p. Latest fashions at attractive prices.

Bergdorf Goodman, 754 Fifth Ave., New York, NY 10019. Free, several throughout year. High fashion clothing and accessories.

Brownstone Studio, 342 Madison Ave., New York, NY 10017. Free, 32p. High quality fashion collection for office or patio.

First Editions, 340 Poplar St., Hanover, PA 17331. Free, 24p. Tasteful contemporary styles for work and play.

Honeybee, 2745 Philmont Ave., Huntingdon Valley, PA 19006. Free, 32p. Latest fashions from swimwear to suits.

Lane Bryant, 2300 Southeastern Ave., Box 7201, Indianapolis, IN 46207. Free, 104p. Good value on fashions, shoes, lingerie for larger women.

Roaman's, Saddle Brook, NJ 07662. Free, 74p. Moderately priced women's clothing, shoes.

Tog Shop, Lester Square, Americus, GA 31710. Free, 128p. Lots of reasonably priced separates, shoes, dresses.

Collectors

Baseball Advertiser (See *Catalogs: Outdoors & Sports.*)

Brooks Stamp Co., Box 62, Homecrest Station, Brooklyn, NY 11229. Free, 36p. U.S. and foreign stamps.

Collector's Choice, Box 12600, Lake Park, FL 33403. $1, 48p. For collectors of thimbles, spoons, music boxes, porcelain figurines, clowns, plates, Hummel or Rockwell art.

Country Store at Centerville, Centerville, Cape Cod, MA 02632. Free, 30p. Many collector's thimbles, spoons, dolls; assorted other gifts.

Downs' Collectors Showcase, 2778 S. 35th St., Milwaukee, WI 53215. 50 cents, 40p. Figurines, plates, thimbles, bells, other gift items.

H.E. Harris & Co., 645 Summer St., Boston, MA 02117. $2.95, 362p. Stamps, albums, supplies.

Jamestown Stamp Co., Jamestown, NY 14701. Free, 64p. Stamps, supplies.

Littleton Stamp & Coin Co., 253 Union St., Littleton, NH 03561. Free, 114p. U.S. stamps, albums, supplies.

Martin Band, 225 W. 34th St., New York, NY 10122. 30 cents, 36p. Worldwide stamp sets, singles.

Palmetto Warehouse, Rt. 1, Hwy. 321, Norway, SC 29113. $3.25, 96p. ($2 refundable and free gift with first order). Americana collectibles and memorabilia, from Coca-Cola, breweries, Hollywood, political campaigns.

Rombins' Nest Farm, Rt. 116 West, Fairfield, PA 17320. Free, 40p. Collectibles, early American items, crafts, toys, dolls.

U.S. Postal Service, General Manager, Philatelic Sales Division, Washington, DC 20265. Free catalogs of stamps and supplies 6 times a year. Ask to be placed on mailing list.

Village Coin Shop, Box 207, Plaistow, NH 03865. 25 cents, 28p. Coins, currency, supplies for the numismatist; supplies for stamp collectors.

Craft Supplies

Artist

Charrette, 31 Olympia Ave., Box 4010, Woburn, MA 01888 $2, 292p. Everything for the architect, draftsman and artist.

Dick Blick, Box 1267, Galesburg, IL 61401. $2, 320p. Artist, printing, drafting supplies.

Hearlihy & Co., 714 W. Columbia St., Springfield, OH 45501. Free, 52p. Industrial drafting and commercial art supplies.

Utrecht, 33 35th St., Brooklyn, NY 11232. Free, 52p. Paints, brushes, canvas, paper, pens, easels, etc.

Assorted

Allcraft Tool and Supply Co., Inc., 100 Frank Rd., Hicksville, NY 11801. $2.50, 134p. Well-stocked catalog for metalsmithing, silversmithing, jewelry making, enameling or casting.

American Handicrafts/Merribee Needlearts, 406 Meyerland Plaza, Houston, TX 77096. Free catalogs throughout year. Needlework kits of all kinds, decoupage, macramé, enameling, string art, casting supplies, etc.

Arthur Brown & Bro., 2 W. 46th St., New York, NY 10036. $3, 228p. Over 20,000 items for fine and graphic artists, engineers, architects, educators.

Craft Service, 337 University Ave., Rochester, NY 14607. $1, 60p. Wide variety of craft materials—leather, batik, macramé, beads, balsa wood, seating, art glass, more.

Herrschners, Inc., Hoover Rd., Stevens Point, WI 54481. Free, 72p. Kits for needlework, glass, ball point paint, string art, Christmas ornaments, latch hook.

Lee Wards, 840 N. State St., Elgin, IL 60120. Free, 72p. Kits for quilts, needlepoint, embroidery, crochet, cross-stitch, latch hook, crewel, and other crafts.

National Artcraft Co., 23456 Mercantile Rd., Beachwood, OH 44122. $3, 384p. Clock movements, lamp kits, jewelry settings, porcelain bisque figurines, decals, etc.

Sanshar Crafts, Box 82, Homecrest Station, Brooklyn, NY 11229. Free, 30p. Supplies for weaving, etching, batik, sculpture, ceramics, graphic arts, lithography; craft books.

Sax Arts & Crafts, Box 2002, Milwaukee, WI 53201. $2, 360p. All kinds of arts and crafts supplies.

Skil-Crafts, 305 Virginia, Joplin, MO 64801. $3, 296p. Supplies for most crafts—tole painting, leather working, candle making, painting, print making, soap craft, etc.

Candlemaking

Barker Enterprises, Inc., 15106 10th Ave., S.W., Seattle, WA 98166. Free, 54p. Molds, candleholders, candle craft supplies. Large selection.

Pourette, Box 15220, Seattle, WA 98115. Free. Candle-making, decorating supplies—many shapes from Buddha to baseballs. Soap-making kits.

Ceramics, Pottery

American Art Clay Co., 4717 W. 16th St., Indianapolis, IN 46222. Free, 76p. Kilns, glazes, wheels, clays, pottery supplies, metal enameling, art craft materials.

Westwood Ceramic Supply Co., 14400 Lomitas Ave., City of Industry, CA 91746. $2, 111p. Clay to kilns.

Clocks

Craft Products Co., 2200 Dean St., St. Charles, IL 60174. $1.50, 100p. Clock kits, movements; dials, etc; music boxes, weather instruments; finished clocks; books.

Mason & Sullivan, 39 Blossom Ave., Osterville, MA 02655. $1, 48p. catalog, supplements. All styles of clock kits, movements, tools for all skill levels.

Enameling

Thompson Enamel, Box 127, Highland Park, IL 60035. $3, 28p. All basic equipment.

Glass

Nervo Distributors, 650 University Ave., Berkeley, CA 94710. $2, 34p. Art, sheet glass; glazier's tools, etc.

S.A. Bendheim Co., 122 Hudson St., New York, NY 10013. Free, 18p. Stained glass, supplies, patterns.

Whittemore-Durgin Glass Co., Box 2065, Hanover, MA 02339. Free, 54p. 50 cents, "Getting Started in Stained Glass." Patterns, supplies, kits for stained glass hobbyist.

Jewelry-Making, Lapidary

Alpha Faceting Supply, Inc., Box 2133, Bremerton, WA 98310. $1, 264p. Rings, stones; machinery, supplies for faceting, casting, lapidary, jewelry making.

Grieger's Inc., 900 S. Arroyo Pkwy., Pasadena, CA 91109. Free, 144p. Jewelry supplies, stones, equipment.

T.B. Hagstoz & Son, 709 Sansom St., Phildelphia, PA 19106. Free, 66p. Tools and supplies for jeweler, craftsman and hobbyist. Also 20p. free catalog of jewelry findings.

Leather

Berman Leathercraft, 147 South St., Boston, MA 02111. $1, 32p. Leathers, tools, belt buckles, dyes, books, sandals, clogs, belts, some finished goods.

Leathercrafters Supply Co., 25 Great Jones (E. 3rd) St., New York, NY 10012. $2, 64p. Leather dyes, tools, kits, hardware.

Tandy Leather Co., Box 791, Ft. Worth TX 76101. $1.50, 124p. Kits for purses, Indian crafts, billfolds; stamps, tools, hardware, books, belt buckles, leather.

Needlework

American Needlewoman, Box 16628, Fort Worth, TX 76133. Free catalog. Kits, books, supplies for latch hook, crewel, needlepoint, cross-stitch.

Better Homes & Gardens Craft Kits, Box 374, Des Moines, IA 50336. Free, 50p. Needlepoint, stitchery, latch hook, quilting, cross-stitch kits.

Elizabeth Zimmermann, Babcock, WI 54413. $1, wool sample card, booklist. Wools from Canada, Iceland, Shetland; pewter buttons, clasps; knitting books.

Family Circle Catalog of Great Samplers, Dept. 070, Box 450, Teaneck, NJ 07666. 50 cents, 32p. Over 300 cross-stitch kits.

Ginger Snap Station, Box 81086, Atlanta, GA 30366. 50 cents, 100p. Quilting, patchwork, calico, appliqué, kits, patterns, and supplies. Beautiful catalog.

Home-Sew, Inc., Bethlehem, PA 18018. Free, 22p. Sewing notions, trims, zippers, laces, craft items.

Jane Snead Samplers, Box 4909, Phiadelphia, PA 19119. 25 cents, 48p. Cross stitch, needlepoint samplers.

Mary Maxim, 2001 Holland Ave., Port Huron, MI 48060. Free, 64p. Needlecraft Kits catalog—baby gifts, quilts, sweaters, latch hook, afghans, more.

Peacock Alley, 650 Croswell St., S.E., Grand Rapids, MI 49506. $2, 20p. Exclusive needlepoint kits.

Shiffcraft, 500 N. Calvert St., Baltimore, MD 21202. Free, 48p. Ready-cut kits for latch-hook wall hangings, pillows, rugs.

Stitch 'n Knit, 1604 Concord St., Framingham, MA 01701. Free, 32p. Pictures, rugs, purses, afghans, ornaments, blouses, etc.; knitting, needlepoint, crochet, crewel, etc.

Stitchery, Wellesley, MA 02181. 50 cents, 80p. Four per year. Nice stitchery, needlepoint kits; some exclusives.

Virginia's Needlecraft Books, Box 1797, Buena Vista, CO 81211. $1, 32p. Interesting choice of books on patterns, crochet, needlepoint, knitting; most on dolls and doll clothes.

Seat Weaving

H.H. Perkins Co., 10 S. Bradley Rd., Woodbridge, CT 06525. Free, 24p. "Seat Weaving for Pleasure and Profit." "Instructions in Methods of Seat Weaving," 25 cents. Natural, plastic cane webbing; chair kits; rush, splint seats; reed kits for doll cradle, baskets; books; beads; accessories.

Weaving

Ayottes' Designery, Center Sandwich, NH 03227. Free brochure. Home study course in weaving.

Contessa Yarns, Box 37, Lebanon, CT 06249. Free samples. Different novelty, straight yarns for handweaving.

Harrisville Designs, Harrisville, NH 03450. $2, brochure, yarn samples. Do-it-yourself (or assembled) hand looms, weaving equipment; virgin wools, camel hair, homespun, handspinning fleeces, linsey-woolsey, wool.

Mannings, The, R.D. 2, East Berlin, PA 17316. 50 cents, 23p. catalog, yarn samples. Looms, spinning wheel, books; rug-making, macramé, basketry, spinning, weaving supplies.

Pendleton Shop, Box 233, Sedona, AZ 86336. Free brochure. Looms, books on weaving, weaving equipment. Notepaper for handweavers.

School Products Co., Inc., 1201 Broadway, New York, NY 10001. $1, 32p. Looms; weaving & spinning equipment, supplies.

Woodworking

See *Catalogs: Handyman.*

Constantine's, 2050 Eastchester Rd., Bronx, NY 10461. $1, 100p. Wood picture kits, doll house furniture kits, veneers, hardwoods, books, supplies.

Craftplans, Industrial Blvd., Rogers, MN 55374. 50 cents, 23p. Plans for weather vanes, furniture, household items, decorations, etc.

Craftsman Wood Service Co., 1735 W. Cortland, Addison, IL 60101. Free, 152p. Over 4,000 items—clock kits, musical instrument kits, power tools, hardwoods, etc.

Love-Built Toys, 2907 Lake Forest Rd., Box 5459, Tahoe City, CA 95730. $1. About 200 designs or kits for wooden toys; supplies, books.

Woodworkers' Store, 21801 Industrial Blvd., Rogers, MN 55374. $1, 116p. A little of everything—hardware, materials, books, etc.

Cycling

Bikecology, 205 S. McKemy St., Chandler, AZ 85224. $1, 32p. Wide range of bikes, accessories, clothing, books.

Touring Cyclist Shop, Box 4009, Boulder, CO 80306. Free, 48p. Touring bags, clothing, safety items, books, plus lots of helpful information on touring.

Electronics

BNF Enterprises, Box 3357, Peabody, MA 01960. Free, 40p. Closeouts and overstocks on computer equipment, photo supplies, cable TV parts, tools, security devices, etc.

Etco, Rt. 9, N, North Country Shopping Center, Plattsburgh, NY 12901. Free, 96p. Crammed full of cable converters, alarm and security devices, test instruments, speaker accessories, relays, much more.

Heathkit, Benton Harbor, MI 49022. Free, 96p. Kits and supplies for computers, stereos, thermostats, etc.

Henshaw's, 7622 Wornall, Kansas City, MO 64114. 50 cents, 64p. Radar detectors, metal detectors, car stereos, CB radios, computers, TV games, etc.

Food

Assorted

Better Foods Foundation, 300 N. Washington St., Greencastle, PA 17225. Free, 6p. No additives in their cereals, flours, beans, nuts, dried fruits, sweeteners, etc.

Creole Delicacies Co., Box 51042, New Orleans, LA 70151. 25 cents, 8p. Pralines, sauces, cane syrup, etc.

Crockett Farms, Box 1150, Harlingen, TX 78551. Free, 14p. Valley fruit gift packs, smoked meats, Texas pecans.

E.M. Todd Co., Box 5167, Richmond, VA 23220. Free leaflets. Smoked ham, bacon; flour, pancake mix, corn meal, etc.

Figi's, 88 Dairy Lane, Marshfield, WI 54404. Free, 80p. Gift packs of cheese, sausage, jams, candy, etc.

Great Valley Mills, Box 260, Quakertown, Bucks County, PA 18951. Free price list. Stoneground flours, smoked meats, preserves, cheese, relishes, butters, honey, crafts.

Harry & David, Bear Creek Orchards, Medford, OR 97501. Free, 16p. Fruit of the Month Club; gift baskets of meats, cheese, candy.

Jaffe Bros., Box 636, Valley Center, CA 92082. Free, 12p. "Organically grown, untreated" dried fruits, nuts, seeds, grains, honey, beans.

Koinonia Partners, Rt. 2, Americus, GA 31709. Free, 40p. Nuts, granola, candy, fruit cakes, books, handcrafts.

The Lambs, Box 520, Libertyville, IL 60048. Free brochure. Reasonably priced gift packs of preserves, cookies, breads, etc. Non-profit organization to help mentally handicapped adults.

Latta's Oregon Delicacies, Box 1377, Newport, OR 97365. Free brochures. Gourmet seafood, hazelnuts, preserves.

Meadowbrook Herbs & Things, Whispering Pines Rd., Wyoming, RI 02898. 50 cents, 28p. Herbal teas, seasonings, seeds, gift packs, syrups, natural cosmetics.

Mrs. Appleyard's Kitchen, Maple Lane, Box 685, Newport, VT 05855. Several free catalogs throughout year. Preservative-free cookies, jams, wholegrain mixes, maple syrup and candies, honey, tea.

Paprikas Weiss Gourmet Shop, 1546 2nd Ave., New York, N.Y. 10028. $1, annual catalog subscription. Imported gourmet foods, cookware.

Pepperidge Farm Mail Order Co., Rt. 145, Clinton, CT 06413. Free, 40p. Baked goods, candy, jam, soup, etc. Top quality.

San Francisco Bay Gourmet, 311 California St., Suite 700, San Francisco, CA 94104. 25 cents, 16p. Bay area specialties of sourdough, cheese, fruit, wine, gift packs and a few gift items.

Sultan's Delight, 409 Forest Ave., Staten Island, NY 10301. Free, 16p. Middle Eastern specialties, spices, cookbooks, belly dancing apparel, gourmet equipment.

Swiss Colony, 112 7th Ave., Monroe, WI 53566. Free, 132p. Gift packs of cheese, sausage, candy, jellies, nuts, gingerbread houses, fruit, ham, etc.

Walnut Acres, Penns Creek, PA 17862. Free, 34p. Any kind of natural food you might imagine; cosmetics, etc.

Wisconsin Cheeseman, Box 1, Madison, WI 53701. Free, 96p. Big assortment of gift packs of cheese, cured meats, sweets, nuts, many in reusable containers.

Cheese

Crowley Cheese, Healdville, VT 05147. Free price list. Cheese, maple syrup.

Sugarbush Farm, RFD No. 2, Woodstock, VT 05091. Free brochure. Natural cheese, pure maple syrup, maple sugar candy.

Coffee, Tea

McNulty's Tea & Coffee Co., 109 Christopher St., New York, NY 10014. Free brochure. Exotic teas, coffees.

Northwestern Coffee Mills, 217 N. Broadway, Milwaukee, WI 53202. Free, 4p. Coffees, teas, spices, nuts, cheeses; coffee and tea pots.

Schapira Coffee Co., 117 W. 10th St., New York, NY 10011. Free leaflet. Exotic coffees, teas, accessories.

Dried

Chuck Wagon Foods, 780 N. Clinton Ave., Trenton, NJ 08638. Free price list. Meal packs, à la carte foods for camping.

Food Reserves, 710 S.E. 17th St., Causeway, Fort Lauderdale, FL 33316. $1, 36p. Dehydrated and freeze-dried foods, bulk grains, beans, legumes, self-sufficiency books, supplies.

Food Storage Sales, 3999 S. Main, Salt Lake City, UT 84107. 50 cents, 12p. Dehydrated foods. Also 32p. Country Catalog of kitchen tools, home canning equipment, how-to books.

Mountain House Freeze-Dried Foods, 3025 Washington Blvd., Ogden, UT 84401. Free, 4p. Variety packs and individual cans of all kinds of foods that require no cooking to prepare.

Fruit

Pioneer Seminole Groves, Cocoa, FL 32922. Free, 16p. Oranges, grapefruit, limes, mangos, avocados.

Italian

Manganaro's, 488 9th Ave., New York, NY 10018. Free, 10p. Meats, cheese, pasta, kitchen utensils, gourmet foods.

Meats

Amana Society Meat Shop, Amana, IA 52203. Free, 8p. Smoked sausage, bacon, ham; gift packs; cheese.

McArthur's Smokehouse, Millerton, NY 12546. Free, 12p. Smoked turkey, ham, bacon, capon, pheasant, lamb, game hens, chicken, sausage

Pfaelzer Brothers, 4501 W. District Blvd., Chicago, IL 60632. Free, 40p. Over 100 meat, seafood, poultry items; gourmet accessories; gift packs.

Schaller & Weber, Inc., 22-35 46th St., Long Island City, NY 11105. Free price lists. Smoked ham, salami, liverwurst, bologna, sausage, cold cuts.

Nuts

Almond Plaza, California Almond Growers Exchange, 1802 C St., Sacramento, CA 95814. Flavored almonds; almonds in candy and fruit cakes.

Pride of Plantation Pecans, Box 729, Leesburg, GA 31763. Free, 8p. Pecans roasted, salted, in decorative tins or jars, and in confections.

Priester's Pecans, 227 Old Fort Dr., Ft. Deposit, AL 36032. Free, 32p. Pecans, candies.

Oriental

Chinese Kitchen, Box 218, Stirling, NJ 07980. 50 cents, 16p. Oriental utensils, foods, cookbooks.

Seafood

Briggs-Way Co., Ugashik, AK 99683. Free fliers. Hand-packed salmon, caviar spread.

Hegg & Hegg, 801 Marine Dr., Port Angeles, WA 98362. Free brochure. Smoked salmon; tuna, sturgeon, shrimp, crab.

Saltwater Farm, York Harbor, ME 03911. Free, 16p. Fresh lobster, crab, shrimp; canned seafoods.

Sweets

Bailey's, 26 Temple Place, Boston, MA 02111. Free brochure. Hand-made chocolates, mints, jellies, fudge, nuts, etc.

Bissinger's, 205 W. 4th St., Cincinnati, OH 45202. 25 cents, 16p. Specialty chocolate, other goodies.

Collin Street Bakery, Corsicana, TX 75110. Free brochure. DeLUXE brand fruit cake, since 1896.

DeSoto Nut House, Box 75, DeSoto, GA 31743. Free brochure. Handmade candy and gift-boxed nuts.

Plumbridge, 33 E. 61st St., New York, NY 10021. Free brochure. Uniquely packaged confections.

Winemaking

Semplex of USA, Box 12276, 4805 Lyndale Ave. N., Minneapolis, MN 55412. Free, 22p. Supplies for amateur wine maker and beer maker.

Vynox Industries, 400 Avis St., Rochester, NY 14615. $2, 59p. Wine and beer-making instructions, supplies.

Gardening

Bountiful Ridge Nurseries, Princess Anne, MD 21853. Free, 32p. Fruit and other trees, vegetables, berries, etc.

Breck's, 6523 N. Galena Rd., Peoria, IL 61632. $1, 84p. Many bulbs from Holland.

Brooklyn Botanic Garden, 1000 Washington Ave., Brooklyn, NY 11225. Free, brochure. Horticulture books.

Burpee Seed Co., Box 2001, Clinton, IA 52732. Free catalogs. Flower and vegetable seeds, grasses, berries, trees, bulbs, tools, garden supplies.

Capability's Books for Gardeners, Rt. 1, Box 114, Hwy. 46, Deer Park, WI 54007. Free, 48p. Wide variety of subjects such as mushrooms, greenhouses, famous gardens, landscaping, plus many on individual plants.

Desert Plant Co., Box 880, Marfa, TX 79843. $1, 36p. All kinds of succulents and desert plants.

Dorothy Biddle Service, Dept. JK, DBS Bldg., Hawthorne, NY 10532. 10 cents, 16p. Flower arranging and house plant supplies, books.

Garden Way Publishing Co. (See *Catalogs: Books.*)

Girard Nurseries, Box 428, Geneva, OH 44041. Free, 36p. Bonsai, shade, ornamental trees; shrubs; azaleas; seeds.

Harris Seeds, Moreton Farm, Rochester, NY 14624. Free, 88p. Vegetable, flower seeds; garden supplies.

Henry Leuthardt Nurseries, Montauk Hwy., East Moriches, NY 11940. $1, 32p. catalog and handbook on dwarf fruit trees, espalier-trained fruit trees, berries, grapes.

Jackson & Perkins Co., Medford, OR 97501. Free brochure. Dutch bulbs—tulip, iris, crocus, daffodil.

Kester's Wild Game Food Nurseries, Box V, Omro, WI 54963. $1, 34p. Seeds, tubers, plants to attract waterfowl, fish, game birds, game animals.

Lilypons Water Gardens, Lilypons, MD 21717. $1.75, 48pp. Water lilies, statuary, fish, water gardening supplies.

Mellinger's, 2310 W. South Range, North Lima, OH 44452. $1, 104p. Many books, seeds, gardening supplies, bulbs, etc.

Nichols Garden Nursery, 1190 N. Pacific Hwy., Albany, OR 97321. Free, 68p. Herb, gourmet vegetable, and other rare seeds; herbal teas, soaps; winemaking supplies.

Park Seed Co., 97 Cokesbury Rd., Greenwood, SC 29647. Free, 124p. Hundreds of flower, vegetable seeds; gardening equipment.

Peter Paul's Nurseries, Canandaigua, NY 14424. Brochure, 25 cents or free with stamped, addressed envelope. Carnivorous and woodland terrarium plants.

R.H. Shumway Seedsman, Box 777, Rockford, IL 61101. Free, 92p. Vast selection of seeds, supplies.

Ringer Research, 6860 Flying Cloud Dr., Eden Prairie, MN 55344. Free, 10p. Organic gardening and lawn products.

Spring Hill, 110 W. Elm St., Tipp City, OH 45371. $1, 84p. Good selection of trees, shrubs, flowers, fruit.

Stark Bro's Nurseries, Box 12178, Louisiana, MO 63353. Free, 66p. Fruit and nut trees (dwarfs, too), berries, bulbs, vines.

Stokes Seeds Inc., Box 548, Buffalo, NY 14240. Free, 156p. All kinds of flowers, vegetable plants, and fruit trees.

Submatic Irrigation Systems, Box 246, Lubbock, TX 79408. Free, 16p. Drip irrigation system parts.

Western Maine Forest Nursery Co., 36 Elm St., Fryeburg, ME 04037. Free brochure. Evergreen trees, shrubs.

Wildlife Nurseries, Box 2724, Oshkosh, WI 54903. $1, 28p. Plants, seeds to attract game birds, wild ducks, deer.

Handcrafts

Andersen Design, Andersen Rd., E. Boothbay, ME 04544. $2, 18p. Hand-crafted stoneware animals, decorative accessories.

Cabin Creek Quilts, Box 383, Cabin Creek, WV 25305. Free, 22p. Cottage industry producing award-winning patchwork quilts, baby quilts, sock dolls, place mats, pillows, wall hangings, clothing.

Camphill Village Gift Shop, Chrysler Pond Rd., Copake, NY 12516. Free brochure. Wooden trivets, toys, enameled copperware, batiks, note cards, woven place mats, etc. Handcrafted by handicapped adults.

Craft Shop at Molly's Pond, Rt. 2, Cabot, VT 05647. 50 cents, 14p. Hand-crafted silver pendants, earrings, pins—most from the world of nature. Simple and lovely.

Freedom Quilting Bee, Rt. 1, Box 72, Alberta, AL 36720. Send addressed, stamped envelope for brochure of locally made quilts.

Goodfellow Catalog of Wonderful Things, Box 4520, Berkeley, CA 94704. $22.45ppd. for 418p. soft-cover book of over 500 crafts (all pictured) you may order directly from the artisans.

Koinonia Partners, Rt. 2, Americus, GA 31709. Free, 40p. Handmade dashikis, pillows, macramé items; food, books.

Laura Copenhaver Industries, Rosemont, Marion, VA 24354. Free, 30p. "Traditional mountain crafts"—handmade furniture, quilts, bed canopies, coverlets, curtains.

Mission Houses Gift Shop, 553 S. King St., Honolulu, HI 96813. Free, 16p. Hawaiian gifts—toys, leis, native crafts, games, jewelry, books.

Plumb Hill Studio, Plumb Hill Rd., Washington, CT 06793. Free brochure. Ornaments, serving pieces, in fused glass, cathedral glass, weedash.

Shep's Ship Shop, Jordan Cove, Waterford, CT 06385. Free flier. Hand-carved figureheads, ship's eagle plaques.
Student Craft Industries, Berea College, Berea, KY 40404. 50 cents, 28p. Needlecraft, weaving, ceramics, lapidary, wrought iron, brooms, note cards, wood craft—all made by students.
Virginia Goodwin, Box 36603, Charlotte, NC 28236. Free brochure. Heirloom quality woven colonial coverlets, canopies.
West Rindge Baskets, Inc., Box 24, Rindge, NH 03461. Free brochure. Hand-woven ash baskets in 16 sizes.
Weston Bowl Mill, Rt. 100, Weston, VT 05161. 35 cents, 32p. Wooden bowls, toys, cutting boards, kitchen utensils, bird feeders, buckets, etc.

Handicapped

Community Playthings, Rifton, NY 12471. Free, 74p. Equipment for handi-capped children in school setting; children's wooden furiture, outdoor equipment, toys, etc.
FashionAble, Rocky Hill, NJ 08553. 50 cents, 8p. Useful items, clothing for disabled, one-handed, wheelchair-bound.
Tytell Typewriter Co. (See *Catalogs: Typewriters*)
Vocational Guidance & Rehabilitation Services, 2239 E. 55th St., Cleveland, OH 44103. $1.50, 54p. Clothing altered for various handicaps. Will cus-tom make garments.
Whitakers, 41 Douglas Ave., Yonkers, NY 10703. Free, 16p. Lifting devices for stairs, chairs, bath, wheelchairs.
Wuensch, 33 Halsted St., East Orange, NJ 07018. 50 cents, 24p. Aids for bed-ridden, wheelchair patients; adjustable beds; exercisers; Norman Dine Sleep Shop; orthopedic shoes.

Handyman

(See *Catalogs: Craft Supplies and Woodworking.*)
American Machine & Tool Co., Inc., 4th & Spring St., Royersford, PA 19468. Free leaflets. Economy power tools—saws, belt sander, wood lathes, motors, jointer-planer, accessories.
Brookstone Co., 127 Vose Farm Rd., Peterborough, NH 03458. Free, 68p. Hard-to-find, often unique, tools for garden, car repair, kitchen, framing, woodworking, etc.
Dick Cepek, 5302 Tweedy Blvd., South Gate, CA 90280. $1, 130p. "World's largest off-road dealer." Tires, parts, camping gear, books.
Energy Savers, Box 99, New Rochelle, NY 10804. $1, 44p. Lots of products to save you energy and dollars.
Gilliom Manufacturing Inc., 1109 N. 2nd St., St. Charles, MO 63301. 50 cents. Plans, kits for average home craftsman to build power wood-working tools, motor cart.
J.C. Whitney & Co., Box 8410, Chicago, IL 60680. $1, 290p. Parts, acces-sories for cars, motorcycles, vans, trucks, RV's.

Leichtung, Inc., 4944 Commerce Parkway, Cleveland, OH 44128. Free, 98p. Tools of all kinds.

National Camera, Inc. (See *Catalogs: Photography.*)

U.S. General Supply Corp., 100 Commercial St., Plainview, NY 11803. $1, 196p. Over 6,000 items of hardware, tools.

Woodline, the Japan Woodworker, 1731 Clement Ave., Alameda, CA 94501. $1, 21p. Finest Japanese saws, chisels, gouges, planes, knives, other tools

Health & Beauty

Bathtique, 161 Norris Dr., Rochester, NY 14610. Free. 24p. Imaginative assortment of shaped soaps, "theme" bath accessories (Crossword Puzzle Toilet Paper), towels.

Beauty Buy Book, 65 E. Southwater, Chicago, IL 60601. Free, 32p. Big savings on famous-name cosmetics, jewelry.

Caswell-Massey Co., Ltd., 575 Lexington Ave., New York, NY 10022. Free, 92p. European cosmetics, beauty supplies, perfumes, more.

Edmund Scientific, 101 E. Gloucester Pike, Barrington, NY 08007. Free, 36p. Health and Fitness catalog. Exercise equipment, books, alarm and safety devices, massagers, blood pressure monitors, etc.

Harvest Health, 1944 Eastern Ave., S.E., Grand Rapids, MI 49507. Free, three catalogs: Vitamins, Herbs and Spices, Book List (health and diet

Hove Parfumeur, 723 Toulouse St., New Orleans, LA 70130. Free, 24p. Perfumes, soaps, men's colognes, etc.

Soap Box at Truc, Box 167, Woodstock, CT 06281. $2 (refundable with first order), 40p. Numerous natural soaps, lotions, shampoos, bath accessories.

Village Bath Products, Box 1-A, Minnetonka, MN 55343. Free brochure. Inexpensive soaps, fragrances, hair care, lip balm. Nice for teens. "Dirty Kids" line for youngsters.

Hearing Impaired

National Association of the Deaf, Publishing Div., 814 Thayer Ave., Silver Spring, MD 20910. Free, 10p. Children's "signed" books and coloring books, jewelry, T-shirts, stationery, instructive books, films, more.

Sign Language Store, Box 4440, 9420 Reseda Blvd., Northridge, CA 91328. 25 cents, 12p. Sign language books, posters, stationery, films, tapes, school supplies, T-shirts, novelties.

Home Furnishings

Ball & Ball, 463 W. Lincoln Hwy., Exton, PA 19341. $4, 100p. Reproductions of American furniture and house hardware, lighting fixtures from 1680 to 1900.

Better Sleep, Inc., New Providence, NJ 07974. 25 cents, 22pp. Pillows, back rests for special needs.

Burning Log, Box 438, Hanover St., Lebanon, NH 03766. Free, catalog being updated. Many accessories for the fireplace.

Country Loft, South Shore Park, Hingham, MA 02043. Free, 40p. Quality Early American furniture, toys, household accessories.

Craft House, Williamsburg, VA 23185. $4.95, 286p. Williamsburg Reproductions—furniture, toys, Delft, fabrics, wallpapers, housewares, silver; 1,800 items.

Fran's Basket House, Rt. 10, Succasunna, NJ 07876. 25 cents, 86p. Furniture, housewares in wicker, rattan, willow.

Guild of Shaker Crafts, 401 W. Savidge, Spring Lake, MI 49456. $2.50, 28p. Authentic replicas of Shaker furniture, stitchery, clothing, accessories.

Leathercrafter, 303 E. 51st St., New York, NY 10022. $1, 32p. with photos, samples. 30 styles of handmade leather chairs, ottomans, benches.

Sturbridge Yankee Workshop, Brimfield Turnpike, Sturbridge, MA 01566. 50 cents, 48p. Furniture, lamps, glassware, dishes, hardware, accessories "in early American tradition."

Wuensch, 33 Halsted St., East Orange, NJ 07018. 50 cents, 24p. Norman Dine Sleep Shop. Adjustable beds, bathroom safety aids, helps for bedridden or handicapped.

Yield House, Box 1000, North Conway, NH 03860. $1, 72p. Early American pine furniture, housewares.

Housewares

China Closet, 6807 Winconsin Ave., Chevy Chase, MD 20015. 25 cents, 36p. Cookware, dishes, kitchen utensils.

Colonial Casting Co., 443 S. Colony St., Meriden, CT 06450. Free, 12p. Handcrafted (leadfree) pewter plates, bowls, candlesticks, etc.

Colonial Garden Kitchens, 270 W. Merrick Rd., Valley Stream, NY 11582. $1, 60p. Utensils, supplies, serving pieces for every kitchen need.

Figi's Collection for Cooking, Marshfield, WI 54404. Free, 60p. Cookware, gourmet accessories, utensils, fresh ideas for the kitchen.

Garden Way, Charlotte, VT 05445. Free, 48p. Country Kitchen catalog. Equipment for home canning, sausage making; dehydrators, juicers, crocks, etc.

Hammacher Schlemmer, 147 E. 57th St., New York, NY 10022. Free, 64p. Gourmet cooking items, linens, other out-of-the-ordinary housewares.

Maid of Scandinavia Co., 3244 Raleigh Ave., Minneapolis, MN 55416. $1, 240p.; 50 cents, 112p. summer catalog. Kitchen utensils; everything for cake decorating; candy molds; cookie cutters; party decorations; books.

Nat Schwartz, 210 East 58th St., New York, NY 10022. Free, 32p. Famous name china, crystal, sterling, stainless flatware, figurines and giftware. Such names as Lenox, Wedgewood, Waterford, Lladro, Dresden and other quality companies.

Pot-pouri-ri, The Stitchery Bldg., 204 Worchester, Wellesley, MA 02181. Free, 64p. Quality housewares, decorative and useful.

Spear Engineering Co., Box 7025, Dept. 1138, Colorado Springs, CO 80933. Free brochures. Personalized day-night lawn or mailbox markers. Also line of desk or door nameplates.

Walter Drake Silver Exchange, Drake Bldg., Colorado Springs, CO 80940. $2.50, 54p. Sterling and Silverplate Flatware Pattern Identification Directory. Free information on how to buy or sell over 2000 silver patterns, some no longer manufactured.

Indian Supplies (crafts)

Bowsers' Indian Arts & Crafts, 1015 E. Florence Blvd., Casa Grande, AZ 85222. Free price list. Authentic American Indian beads, belt buckles, jewelry, pottery, etc.

Four Winds Indian Trading Post, St. Ignatius, MT 59865. $1, 12p. American Indian moccasins, beadwork, knife sheaths, books, handbags, blanket coats, etc.

Grey Owl Indian Craft Manufacturing Co., 113–15 Springfield Blvd., Queens Villge, NY 11429. 50 cents, 128p. Supplies, kits for headdresses, leather-crafts, Indian princess dress, etc.; Indian records, books; finished bead-work; make-up.

Plume Trading and Sales Co. Inc., Box 585, Monroe, NY 10950. 50 cents, 36p. Headdresses, feathers, craft supplies, vests, leggings, beaded articles, bustles, books, records, kits, handcrafts.

Supernaw's Oklahoma Indian Supply, Box 216, Skiatook, OK 74070. $1, 72p. Beads, feathers, skins; tools, supplies for silversmiths, jewelers, metal workers, casters, lapidaries; Indian books, records.

International Goods

Bremen House, 218 E. 86th St., New York, NY 10028. Free, 20p. Gourmet foods from around the world; German periodicals, records, gifts; European cosmetics.

Greek Island Ltd., 215 E. 49th St., New York, NY 10017. Free, 36p. Mostly Greek clothing, jewelry, books, decorative items.

Gump's, 250 Post St., San Francisco, CA 94108. $1, 80p. Fine gifts from the world over. Dinnerware, serving items, jewelry, bronzes, art objects.

Icemart, Mail Order Dept., Keflavik International Airport, 235 Iceland. Free, 36p. Superb sweaters, blankets, coats, caps, socks, mittens, sweater kit, in light-weight Icelandic wool. Also sterling jewelry, sheepskin rugs.

Maggie's Irish Imports, 372 Virginia St., Crystal Lake, IL 60014. Free, 20p. Wonderful Irish sweaters, jewelry, books, Belleek, Waterford crystal, etc.

Scotland by the Yard, Rt. 4, Quechee, VT 05059. Free brochure. "Importers of everything Scottish." Tartan ties and cloth, kilts, jewelry, pottery, etc.

The Scottish Lion, North Conway, NH 03860. $1, 48p. Tartan ties, Buchan Thistle pottery, Edinburgh crystal, and other lovely gift items.

Shopping International, Norwich, VT 05055. Free, 48p. Lovely gifts from around the world—jewelry, clothing, seasonal decorations.

Jewelry

(See *Catalogs: Smorgasbord; Art and Special Treasures*)
A.G.A. Correa, Box 401, Wiscasset, ME 04578. Free, 32p. Fine 14K and 18K jewelry, most with nautical themes. A few other marine gift items.
James Avery Craftsman, Inc., Box 1367, Kerrville, TX 78028. Free, 18p. Lovely sterling and 14K gold jewelry with many designs from nature or religious symbols.
Jewelart Inc., 16734 Stagg St., Van Nuys, CA 91406. 25 cents, 60p. Wide selection for adults, children. Affordable.
Kenya Gem, Day & Frick, 1760 N. Howard St., Philadelphia, PA 19122. Free, 16p. Simulated diamond jewery.
Merrin, 724 5th Ave., New York, NY 10019. Free, 64p. Fine jewelry, many distinctive designs.
Mignon Faget Ltd., 710 Dublin St., New Orleans, LA 70118. Free, 20p. "Sea & Earth" fine jewelry with semi-precious stones, shells. Lovely.
Monseratte, Box 65, Bellport, NY 11713. Free, 16p. Hat tacks, clips, key chains, pendants with sporting motifs from skiing to golf to bowling.

Lefties

Aristera, The Left Hand People, Box 2224, Woburn, MA 01888. $1, 16p. Lefty Survival Manual. Ordinary items made for left-handed—scissors, cards, watch, tools, utensils, writing supplies. Also Lefty Pride T-shirts, tote bags, etc.
Left Hand Plus, Box 1204, Aurora, IL 60507. $1 (refundable), 10p. Utensils, instruction manuals, watches, writing aids, etc.
Left Is! Ltd., Box 324, Hinsdale, Ill. 60521. $1, 8p. Clothing, jewelry with "lefty" logos. Scissors, playing cards for left-handed.

Models & Miniatures

(See *Catalogs: Toys & Games.*)
America's Hobby Center, Inc., 146 W. 22nd St., New York, NY 10011. 8 big catalogs on model railroads, airplanes, boats, cars. Up to $1.50 each. Wide choice of kits and supplies. Write for complete list.
Cir-Kit Concepts, 608 N. Broadway, Rochester, MN 55901. $3, 28p. "To scale" lamps, fixtures, tools, supplies for miniature electrical equipment.
Craft Creative Kits, Dept. 70, 2200 Dean St., Charles, IL 60174. $1, Doll House Catalog. 1,500 accessories for doll houses; plans, kits; wall, floor coverings.
Dollhouse Antics Inc., 1308 Madison Ave., New York, NY 10028. $2, 64p. Furniture, accessories.
Enchanted Doll House, 16022 Deer Meadow, Manchester Center, VT 05255. $2, 64p. Doll house kits, furniture, books, accessories. $1, for general catalog of toys, dolls.

House of Miniatures, Box 1816, Santa Fe, NM 87501. Free, 7p. Handcrafted adobe style dollhouses and accessories.

It's A Small World, 555 Lincoln Ave., Winnetka, IL 60093. $4.50, 76p. Miniature furniture, silver, china, etc.

James Bliss & Co., 100 Rt. 128, Dedham, MA 02026. Free, 96p. Marine models, fittings, engines; doll furniture; tools.

Lynne's Miniature Treasures, Dept. 22, North Wales, PA 19454. Free, 64p. Miniature furniture, accessories.

Miniature Shop, 1115 Fourth Ave., Huntington, WV 25701. $2.50, 182p. Dollhouses, building supplies, accessories, tools, kits.

Northeastern Scale Models, Box 425Q, Methuen, MA 01844. Send long, stamped, addressed envelope for catalog, or $2 for catalog & samples. Doll house building materials.

Pinchpenny Minitures, 17 Idaho Lane, Matawan, NJ 07747. 75 cents, 20p. General store, dollhouse furniture and accessories at good prices.

Polk's Model Craft Hobbies, 314 5th Ave., New York, NY 10001. $4.95, 196p. Very complete assortment of models, kits of ships, airplanes, cars, trains, and everything that goes with them. Military, doll miniatures; rockets, R/C cars; craft supplies.

Movies

Audio Brandon Films, 34 MacQuesten Parkway S., Mt. Vernon, NY 10550. Free, 416p. 16mm films for rent—classics, current titles, cartoons; 588p. of international classics; 414p. of general entertainment movies; educational films.

Blackhawk Film Digest, Box 3990, Davenport, IA 52808. Free, 80p. Sells reprints of old movies. Also offers movie history books, slides, posters; projectors; video cassettes.

Reel Images, 495 Monroe TPK, Monroe, CT 06468. $3, 2 catalogs, 150p. Over 500 movies on 8mm, 16mm, video. Classics from 1904, avant garde, foreign, Westerns, animated, etc.

Thunderbird Films, Box 65157, Los Angeles, CA 90065. Free, 32p. 16mm, Super 8, silent, and video tapes of cartoons, Westerns, Laurel & Hardy, documentaries, musicals, experimental films and more.

Walt Disney Home Movies, 500 S. Buena Vista St., Burbank, CA 91521. Free, 14p. Super 8 Disney color movies in English, Portugese, Spanish, or silent.

Music

(See *Catalogs: Audio.*)

Chesterfield Music Shops, Inc., 12 Warren St., New York, NY 10007. Free, 16p. LPs, cassettes of all kinds of music. Some books.

G. Schirmer, 866 3rd Ave., New York, NY 10022. Free, 334p. Huge selection of sheet music—choral (sacred, secular), orchestra, vocal, band, chamber, instrumental, piano, organ, etc.

House of Oldies, 267 Bleecker St., New York, NY 10014. $1.50, 32p. price list. Any 45 r.p.m. record made since 1949.

Hughes Dulcimer Co., 4419 W. Colfax Ave., Denver, CO 80204. Free, 8p. Kits or finished dulcimers, guitars, banjos, mandolins, other stringed instruments.

Indian House, Box 472, Taos, NM 87571. Free price list. American Indian music on LPs, cassettes, or 8-track.

Library of Congress, Central Service Division, Washington, DC 20540. Free "Publications in Print." Mostly books; includes several pages of folk and music recordings (regional, ethnic, tales) and literary recordings (i.e., Robert Frost or T. S. Eliot reading their own poetry).

Music in Motion, Box 5564, Richardson, TX 75080. $1, 24p. Materials for music teachers; music for children; gifts for the musical.

National Library Service for the Blind and Physically Handicapped, Library of Congress, Washington, DC 20542. Free catalogs. Specify Braille scores catalog for choral, organ, piano, or voice; instructional cassette recordings catalog; instructional disc recordings catalog; or large-print scores and books catalog.

Rhythm Band, Inc., Box 126, Fort Worth TX 76101. Free, 34p. Musical instruments, records. Made for elementary schools, but available to individuals.

Spanish Music Center, 319 W. 48th St., New York, NY 10036. $3, several catalogs. Printed music, LPs, cassettes, 8-track Latin American and Spanish music; much guitar.

Outdoors & Sports

Akers Ski, Andover, ME 04216. Free, 32p. "Nordic specialists." Skis, outerwear, accessories.

Antelope Camping Equipment, 21740 Granada, Cupertino, CA 95014. 25 cents, 20p. Child, adult pack frames, bags.

Austad's, 4500 E. 10th St., Box 1428, Sioux Falls, SD 57101. Free, 64p. Large selection of golf, tennis, exercise, lawn game, basketball, baseball, soccer, water skiing equipment; tents; sportswear.

Baseball Advertiser, T.C.M.A. Ltd., Box 2, Amawalk, NY 10501. Free, 72p. Baseball cards, stickers, albums, books.

Bay Country Woodcrafts, U.S. Route 13, Oak Hall, VA 23416. $1, 32p. Wooden waterfowl carvings, kits; carving tools; books on decoys; decorative accessories; gifts with wildlife designs.

Bike/Sports Nashbar, 215 Main St., Box 290, New Middletown, OH 44442. Free, 48p. Bicycles, parts, accessories; bike camping gear; books.

Boy Scouts of America, Box 175, Bellwood, IL 60104. Free, 48p. Camping equipment, books; plus Scout uniforms, crafts, gift items

Cabela's, 812 13th Ave., Sidney, NE 69162. Free, 78p. Quality merchandise for fishing, hunting, camping.

Campmor, Box 407CC, Bogota, NJ 07603. Free, 88p. A little bit of everything for campers; also trail food and books.

Cannondale, 35 Pulaski St., Stamford, CT 06902. Free, 22p. Backpacking, bicycling equipment; sleeping bags, vests.

The Crossroads of Sport, Inc., 5 E. 47th St., New York, NY 10017. Free, 82p. Fine art paintings, etchings with outdoor themes; china, carvings, books, housewares with sporting motifs.

Don Gleason's Campers Supply, Box 87, Northampton, MA 01060. 75 cents, 80p. Good selection of camping and backpacking equipment.

Doug Kittredge Bow Hut, Box 598, Mammoth Lakes, CA 93546. Free, 188p. "Archer's Bible." Everything for bow hunting; tents, outdoor clothing, knives, etc.

Eastern Mountain Sports, Inc., Two Vose Farm Rd., Peterborough, NH 03458. Free, 114p. Outdoor clothing, tents, soft luggage, sleeping bags, cooking equipment, much more.

Eddie Bauer, 5th & Union, Box 3700, Seattle, WA 98124. Free, 114p. Well-known source for top quality outdoor apparel, equipment.

Eureka! Tent Inc., 625 Conklin Rd., Box 966, Binghamton, NY 13902. Free, 24p. Over 30 tent styles.

Frostline Kits, Frostline Circle, Denver, CO 80241. Free, 46p. Sew-it-yourself kits for outdoor equipment, clothing. Packs, tents, sleeping bags, parkas; child's sizes, too.

Gander Mountain, Inc., Box 248, Wilmot, WI 53192. Free, 108p. Outdoor sportsman's supplies, tents, guns, clothing; reloading equipment.

Great Pacific Iron Works, Box 150, Ventura, CA 93002. $1, 56p. Rock and ice climbing gear, clothing.

Happy Jack All Outdoors, Dept. C, Snow Hill, NC 28580. Free, 16p. Clothing, accessories for the hunter and his dog.

Hills' Court, Manchester, VT 05254. Free, 36p. Accessories, clothing for tennis, beach, golf, running.

Holubar Mountaineering, Ltd., 6287 Araphoe, Box 7, Boulder, CO 80306. Free, 32p. Outerwear, tents, packs, supplies; kits for making sleeping bags, tents, etc.

L. L. Bean, Freeport, ME 04033. Free catalogs. Large selection of casual clothing; some cycling, camping gear.

Moor & Mountain, 63 Park St., Andover, MA 01810. Free, 64p. Equipment and books on cycling, backpacking, cross-country skiing; canoes; food; much more.

Netcraft, 2800 Tremainsville Rd., Toledo, OH 43613. Free, 174p. Basic fishing gear with emphasis on make-your-own nets, lures, flies, etc.

New England Divers, 131 Rantoul St., Beverly, MA 01915. Free, 32p. Full line of gauges, masks, dry suits, knives, books and other diving equipment.

North Face, Box 2399, Station A, Berkeley, CA 94702. Free, 30p. Packs, tents, sleeping bags, outerwear, etc.

Orvis, 10 River Rd., Manchester, VT 05254. Free, 102p. Everything for fishermen; outdoor clothing and tasteful gift accessories.

P&S Sales, Box 45095, Tulsa, OK 74145. Free, 96p. Attractive assortment of all-weather gear, knives, camping supplies, books.

Port Canvas Co., Dock Square, Kennebunkport, ME 04046. Free, 30p. Canvas bags for many needs, jackets, hammocks, caps, sweaters, etc.

Pro Team Corner, North Towne Plaza Shopping Center, 3600 N. Main St., Rockford, IL 61103. $1, 28p. Posters, glassware, T-shirts, clocks, other items with team logos. NFL, MLB and 90 colleges represented.

Recreational Equipment, Inc., 1525 11th Ave., Box 88125, Seattle, WA 98188. Free, 86p. Backpacking, sports, cycling, outdoor gear and clothing; patterns, kits for outdoor clothing; dried food.

Sierra Designs, 247 Fourth St., Box 12930, Oakland, CA 94604. Free, 48p. Tents, packs, sleeping bags, parkas, vests.

Ski Hut, Box 309, 1615 University Ave., Berkeley, CA 94701. Free, 95p. Outdoor clothing; supplies for boaters, climbers, joggers, campers.

Sportpages, 3373 Towerwood Dr., Dallas, TX 75234. Free, 36p. Fashions accessories for golf, jogging, tennis, etc; gift items.

Sportsman's Guide, 1415 5th St. South, Hopkins, MN 55343. Free, 52p. Pages of novelty T-shirt imprints, belts, buckles; truck accessories; some hunting equipment.

Tennis Discount Shop, 3015 Commercial Ave., Northbrook, IL 60062. Free, 8p. Supplies for the serious tennis player.

Wild Wings, S. Hwy. 61, Lake City, MN 55041. $2.50, 40p. Limited edition wildlife prints, sculptures; other gifts with sporting theme.

Photography

Frank's Highland Park Camera, 5715 N. Figueroa St., Los Angeles, CA 90042. $2, 100p. Complete line of camera and darkroom equipment.

Miko Photo & Sound Co., 1259 Santa Monica Mall, Santa Monica, CA 90401. Free, 100p. Cameras, lenses, books; movie, studio, darkroom, video equipment; accessories.

Modernage Photographic Services, 321 E. 44th St., New York, NY 10017. Free, 20p. Full service photographic lab. Miniature negatives to photo murals.

National Camera, Inc., 2000 W. Union Ave., Englewood, CO 80110. Free, 64p. Camera repair supplies, test instruments, precision and power tools.

Norman Camera, 3602 S. Westnedge, Kalamazoo, MI 49008. Free, 84p. Well-known brands of cameras, equipment, chemicals.

Porter's Camera Store, Box 628, Cedar Falls, IA 50613. Free, 72p. Complete selection of cameras, darkroom equipment, and specialty accessories.

Solar Cine Products, 4247 S. Kedzie, Chicago, IL 60632. Free, 56p. Cameras, projectors, darkroom equipment, books.

Spiratone, 135–06 Northern Blvd., Flushing, NY 11354. "50 cents (to owners of advanced cameras who state name of their camera or camera they want to buy gift for)," 36p. catalog. Lenses, camera accessories, darkroom equipment.

Superior Bulk Film Co., 402 N. Wells St., Chicago, IL 60610. 25 cents, 88p. Film, projectors, home-processing and editing equipment; special services for silent or sound 8mm, Super 8, 16mm, 35mm.

Testrite, 135 Monroe St., Newark, NJ 07105. Free, 48p. Slide copier, lighting accessories, enlarger equipment; other out-of-the-ordinary darkroom supplies.

Science

Edmund Scientific Co., 101 E. Gloucester Pike, Barrington, NJ 08007. $1, 92p. Intriguing collection of scientific equipment for children to professionals. Optics, telescopes, kits, holograms, lenses, biofeedback equipment, jumping discs, visual effects, weather instruments, etc.

Jack Ford Science Projects, Box 948, Duluth, GA 30136. 75 cents, 40p. Out-of-the-ordinary science projects! Plans for sonic generator, invisible force field, laser pistol; 70 more.

Smorgasbord

Abbey Press, 31 Hill Dr., St. Meinrad, IN 47577. $1, 36p. Christian wall hangings, jewelry, records, decorations, housewares, much more.

Adam York, 340 Poplar St., Hanover, PA 17331. Free, 64p. Unusual gifts of jewelry, clothing; accessories for desk, kitchen, etc.

Alden's, 5000 W. Roosevelt Rd., Chicago, IL 60607. Free, 276p. Department store selection of family clothing, linens, small appliances, etc.

Ambassador Shop, 711 W. Broadway, Tempe, AZ 85282. Free, 120p. Good prices on women's clothing, purses, housewares, travel accessories.

American Gift House, 770 E. Sahara Ave. Las Vegas, NV 89104. Free, 32p. Everything in this varied collection is made in America, from the tooth fairy pillows to the electric car.

Blue Chip Gifts, Box 6748, Lubbock, TX 79413. Free catalogs, 24p. for investors; 32p. for petroleum industry. From a Wall Street jigsaw puzzle to a brass solar-powered pumping unit for the desk. Quality and ingenuity. Also great source of Texan gifts.

Bluebook for Brides, 3200 S.E. 14 Ave., Fort Lauderdale, FL 33316. Free, 32p. Complete wedding accessories from invitations to car decorating kit!

Boston Museum Shop, Museum of Fine Arts, Box 1044, Boston, MA 02210. 50 cents, 48p. Jewelry, decorative items, art jigsaw puzzles, stationery.

Brentano's, CB 4048, Huntington Station, NY 11746. Free, 36p. Upbeat gifts such as Sherlock Holmes bookmark, Garfield paraphernalia, musical jewel box, all of top quality.

Brookstone, 5 Vose Farm Rd., Peterborough, N.H. 03458. Free, 48p. Distinctive collection of gifts, including silverplate spoon straws, monogrammed license plate, zebrawood kaleidoscope and other unusual housewares and decorative items.

Bruce Bolind, 5421 Western, Boulder, CO 80302. $1, 80p. Unusual medium-priced gifts, personalized stickers, housewares.

Camalier & Buckley, 1141 Connecticut Ave. N.W., Washington, DC 20036. Free, 32p. Unusual clothing, housewares, gift items.

Charles Keath, Ltd., 4030 Pleasantdale Rd., N.E., Atlanta, GA 30340. Free, 36p. Fine gifts of jewelry, toys, housewares.

Clymer's of Buck County, 141 Canal St., Nashua, NH 03061. 50 cents, 48p. Interesting holiday decorations, housewares, sculpture, knick-knacks, etc.

Deluxe Saddlery, 1817 Whitehead Rd., Baltimore, MD 21207. Free, 96p. Eclectic assortment of gifts, many for sportsmen and horselovers.

Discovery House, 404 Irvington St., Pleasantville, NY 10570. Free, 64p. Items for kitchen, car, boat, hobbies.

FHI Folio, Inc., 1350 Manufacturing St. 108, Dallas, TX 75207. Free, 24p. Nice assortment of gifts.

Foley's Dept. Store, Attn: Direct Mail, Box 1971, Houston, TX 77001. Free catalogs. Housewares, linens, clothing, gifts, etc.

Gokeys, 84 S. Wabasha St., St. Paul, MN 55107. Free, 52p. Nice collection of sporty clothes for men and women; soft luggage; outdoor-type gifts.

Griffin, Ltd., Box 2620, Estes Park, CO 80517. Free, 36p. Carefully selected fashions, housewares, toys.

Hamakor Judaica, Box 59453, Chicago, IL 60659. Free, 48p. "The source for everything Jewish." Books, jewelry, equipment for religious celebrations, toys, humorous gifts.

Happi Faces, Box 2087, W. Peabody, MA 01960. 50 cents, 12p. Hand-painted original designs to be personalized for pictures. Cute for children's room, bath, kitchen, or family room.

Harriet Carter, North Wales, PA 19454. Free, 96p. Inexpensive assortment of gadgets, housewares, gifts.

Henniker's, Box 567, Milwaukee, WI 53201. Free, 32p. Unusual gifts of quality, such as personalized gear shift knob, remote control unit for appliances, table-sized shuffleboard.

Hog Wild!, 280 Friend St., Boston, MA 02114. $1, 16p. Pigs on ski hats, tote bags, tennis skirts, even Calvin Swine jeans.

Horchow Collection, Box 34257, Dallas, TX 75234. $3 for 10 64-page catalogs through the year. Unique, fine quality gifts, jewelry, housewares.

Jenifer House, New Marlboro Stage, Great Barrington, MA 01230. Free, 88p. Americana—housewares, furniture, dishes, "country clothes," nostalgia.

Joan Cook, Box 21628, Ft. Lauderdale, FL 33335. Free, 96p. Nice variety of housewares, decorative items, giftware.

Kaplan's-Ben Hur, P.O. Box 7466, Houston, TX 77248. Free, 48p. High quality serving, decorative gift items.

Karen Studios, Box 175, Rye, NY 10580. Free brochure with self-addressed, stamped envelope. Ceramic ashtray, cookie plate, cigarette box, other items decorated with your artwork. Clever way to personalize gifts.

Landfall Collection, Box 2525, North Conway, NH 03860. Free, 32p. Enchanting collection of women's clothing and gifts.

Lillian Vernon, 510 S. Fulton Ave., Mt. Vernon, NY 10550. Free, 116p. Housewares, toys, jewelry. Reasonable prices, good quality.

Lincoln House, 2015 Grand Ave., Kansas City, MO 64108. Free, 64p. Reasonably priced, unusual gift items, candles, stationery, toys, household helpers.

Miles Kimball Co., 41 W. 8th Ave., Oshkosh, WI 54906. Free, 80p. A little of everything. Personalized bumper stickers, collector's albums, toys; yard, kitchen, cleaning items, desk gadgets, etc.

Monogram Shop, 8900 Shoal Creek Dr., Box 10069, Austin, TX 78766. Free, 16p. Monograms reproduced on clothing, director's chairs, and other gift items.

Museum of the City of New York, 5th Ave. at 103rd St., New York, NY 10029. Free, 16p. Books, prints, toys, unusual gift items.

The Nature Company, Box 7137, Berkeley, CA 94707. Free, 32p. Fascinating collection of gifts from and about nature. Geodes, pocket microscope, books, children's kits, jewelry; many other wonderful gifts.

Neiman-Marcus Co. Mail Order Div., Box 2968, Dallas, TX 75221. $10 for year's catalog subscription. Unusual gifts (some costing thousands of dollars); housewares, clothing, toys, etc.

New Hampton General Store, RFD Hanover, PA 17331. Free, 64p. Low-to-medium priced housewares, decorative items.

Old Guilford Forge, Guilford, CT 06437. 50 cents, 80p. Intriguing collection of early American furniture, brassware, figurines, decorative accessories.

Old Village Shop, 340 Popular St., Hanover, PA 17331. 50 cents, 64p. Interesting assortment of clothing, housewares and gift ideas.

Panorama, 11427 W. 48th Ave., Wheat Ridge, CO 80003. Free, 80p. Variety of affordable gift items, housewares.

The Paragon, 35 High St., Westerly, RI 02891. Free, 68p. Elegant gifts, clothing, home furnishings, gourmet items.

Pennsylvania Station, 340 Poplar St., Hanover, PA 17331. 50 cents, 34p. Wide variety of sophisticated gifts, women's fashions, decorative items.

Propinquity, 8915 Santa Monica Blvd., West Hollywood, CA 90069. Free, 32p. Unusual, humorous gifts, housewares in Art Deco and Art Nouveau tradition.

Sakowitz, Box 1431, Houston, TX 77001. Free, 55p. Housewares, clothing, linens, gifts from a fashionable department store.

Sleepy Hollow Gifts, 6651 Arlington Blvd., Falls Church, VA 22042. Free, 96p. Refreshingly different gifts for all interests, in middle price range.

Spiegel, 1061 W. 35th St., Chicago, IL 60609. Free, 68p. or $3 (refundable with first order), 508p. Fashions, home furnishings, camping gear, everything from the department store.

Suburbia, 366 Wacouta, St. Paul, MN 55101. Free, 96p. Some out-of-the-ordinary toys, housewares, gifts.

Sundials & More, New Ipswich, NH 03071. Free, 36p. Sundials, housewares, clothing, jewelry, gardening aids.

Sunset House, 282 Sunset Bldg., Beverly Hills, CA 90215. Free, 96p. Gadgets, housewares, toys.

Taylor Gifts, Box 206, Wayne, PA 19087. 25 cents, 96p. Big assortment of housewares, toys, jewelry, gifts, etc.

Travelife, Box 1692, 3825 W. Green Tree Rd., Milwaukee, WI 53201. Free, 24p. Gifts for the traveler.

Trifles, Box 44432, Dallas, TX 75234. $2 for 10 64-page color catalogs. Impressive jewelry, housewares, gift items.

Unicorn Gallery, Box 4405, Colesville, MD 20904. Free, 32p. Distinctive gifts, clothing, decorative items—many with unicorn design.

Vermont Country Store, Weston, VT 05161. 25 cents, 98p. Housewares, beauty aids, food, clothing.

The Very Thing, Box 7427, Charlottesville, VA 22906. Free, 32p. Carefully selected women's fashions plus some clever gift items with outdoor or sport motifs.

Vintage Newspapers, Box 48621, Los Angeles, CA 90048. Free brochure. Authentic newspapers or magazines from special day of your choice. Limited quantities and titles.

Walter Drake, HG 71 Drake Bldg., Colorado Springs, CO 80940. Free, 96p. Housewares, utensils, small inexpensive gift items.

Wretched Mess Catalog, 357 MacArthur Blvd., Oakland, CA 94610. 37½ cents, 16p. That should give you a clue as to the tone of this catalog. Wacky, mostly adult cards, posters, gag gifts, old radio shows on cassette.

Writewell Co., 108 Massachusetts Ave., Boston, MA 02115. Free, 32p. Personalized memos, cards, stationery. Also albums for collectors of post cards, matches, wine labels; old time radio shows on cassettes; humor books; other gift ideas.

Stationery

American Stationery Co., Park Ave., Peru, IN 46970. Free, 16p. Personalized stationery, notes, address labels, etc. Good value.

Current, Inc., Current Bldg., Colorado Springs, CO 80941. Free, 48p. Nice quality and prices on pretty stationery, notes, placemats, children's scrapbooks and calendars, wrapping paper, etc. Innovative pricing policy.

Evergreen Press, Box 4971, Walnut Creek, CA 94596. Free, 16p. Bookmarks, bookplates, children's books, Shakespearean greeting cards.

Kristin Elliott, Inc., Box 23, Beverly, MA 01915. Free, 40p. Notes, post cards, gift enclosures, memos with many specialty motifs such as music, tennis, dancing, nautical, etc.

U.S. Committee for UNICEF, Box 5050, G.C.S., New York, NY 10161. Free, 20p. Christmas cards, calendars, games, stationery, books, records.

Writewell Co., (See *Catalogs: Smorgasbord*)

Toys & Games

Bear-in-mind, 73 Indian Pipe Lane, Concord, MA 01742. $1, 48p. Stuffed bears; bears on notecards, sheets, mugs, etc.

Child Life Play Specialties, Inc., 55 Whitney St., Holliston, MA 01746. Free, 24p. Wooden outdoor play equipment—swing sets, jungle gyms, playhouses, etc.

Childcraft, 20 Kilmer Rd., Edison, NJ 08817. Free, 48p. Sturdy, innovative toys and games for babies, kids, and "grown-up" kids.

Community Playthings, Rifton, NY 12471. Free, 74p. Wooden riding toys, storage units, children's furniture, outdoor equipment, equipment for handicapped in school setting. Built for institutions, so very sturdy.

Constructive Playthings, 1040 E. 85th St., Kansas City, MO 64131. $1, 183p. Everything from scissors to swing sets—dolls, nature study, reading readiness materials, games, puzzles, books, outdoor play equipment, etc.

Dick Blick, Box 1267, Galesburg, IL 61401. $2, 576p. Early learning materials, art supplies.

F A O Schwartz, Box 218, Parsippany, NJ 07054. Free, 52p. Delightful array of toys, games, books, records, tapes.

Game Room, Box 4290, Washington, DC 20012. Free, 70p. Gag gifts, humorous "toys" for adults and children.

Johnson Smith World of Fun, 35075 Automation Dr., Mt. Clemens, MI 48043. Free, 96p. Inexpensive novelties, iron-ons, magic, toys.

Just for Kids!, Winterbrook Way, Meredith, NH 03253. Free, 34p. Quality toys, games, baby equipment.

Kathy Kolbe Collection, 3421 N. 44th St., Phoenix, AZ 85018. Free, 16p. Books, games, tapes, brain teasers, puzzles full of academic challenge and mental stimulation for gifted children.

Learning Games, Box 820-C, N. White Plains, NY 10603. Send self-addressed, stamped #10 envelope for brochure on math-related games for preschoolers and older: Quick Master Chess, Domodots, Geoboard Kit, Cuisenaire Home Mathematics Kit.

Mapac Toy Co., Box 454, Bellmore, NY 11710. Free, 4p. Teachers' catalog of student incentives and motivators (stickers, pencil tops, toys, sugarless candy)—very inexpensive.

Marshall Brodien's Magic Catalog, Box 111, Palatine, IL 60067. $2, 96p. Hundreds of magic tricks, many inexpensive.

Milo Products Corp., Grantham, PA 17027. Free brochures. Interlocking wood blocks; beginner sewing kit—made for schools, so they are sturdy.

Mountain Craft Shop (Dick Schnacke's), American Ridge Rd., Rt. 1, New Martinsville, WV 26155. Free brochure. 142 kinds of authentic American folk toys. Makes everyone a kid again.

U.S. Games Systems, 38 E. 32nd St., New York, NY 10016. $1, 40p. Fascinating assortment of tarot decks, magic cards, children's card games, historical and rare decks, etc.

United States Chess Federation, 186 Route 9W, New Windsor, NY 12550. Free, 8p. Computer chess games; chess sets, books, supplies.

Wallace Doll Hospital, 6511 W. Roosevelt Rd., Berwyn, IL 60402. Request specific information on having antique or old dolls refurbished, restrung, or refinished; doll clothes made to order; or doll wigs made or recurled.

Wonders, Box 1348, Beaufort, SC 29902. Free, 32p. "Fine classic toys for the home." Sturdy, long-lasting.

World Wide Games, Box 450, Delaware, OH 43015. $1, 28p. Game tables, sturdy wooden games form around the world, some suitable for visually impaired.

Typewriters

Tytell Typewriter Co., 116 Fulton St., New York, NY 10038. Free brochure. Typewriters in 145 languages; for disabled; special purposes from $\frac{1}{32}$ in. to $\frac{1}{2}$ in. TV prompter. Also many technical keyboards.

Visually Impaired

(See *Catalogs: Audio.*)

American Foundation for the Blind, 15 W. 16th St., New York, NY 10011. Attn: Aids & Appliances. Free, 144p. Watches, canes, instruments, medical aids, writing aids, games, kitchen items, etc. Braille and printed editions. Lists other sources of Braille aids and information.

Library of Congress, Service for the Blind and Physically Handicapped, Washington, DC 20542. Free, 78p. "Talking Books Topics." All kinds of books and magazines for all ages. Discs, cassettes, Braille. Free postage to qualified persons.

Science for the Blind Products, Box 385, Wayne, PA 19087. Free, 40p. Technical aids, toys, games for visually impaired. Recorded catalog available on request.

World Wide Games (see *Catalogs: Toys & Games*)

Western

Equestrian Imports, 13651 Tea House, Santa Ana, CA 92705. Free, 24p. A wonderful collection of horses, unicorns and cowboys on baby quilts, dishes, bookends and other gift items.

Fun-Wear Brands, Box 2800, Estes Park, CO 80517. Free, 32p. Western, Indian clothes and moccasins.

Kauffman, H., & Sons, 139–141 E. 24th St., New York, NY 10010. $1, 72p. English and Western riding clothes, saddles, horseman's accessories, books, gifts with horse motif; racing, polo, blacksmith equipment.

Libertyville Saddle Shop, Box M, Libertyville, IL 60048. $3, 192p. Wide selection of horsemen's supplies, saddlery, and riding apparel.

Miller Stockman, Box 5407, Denver, CO 80217. Free, 80p. Hats, boots, jeans, Western shirts, belt buckles, gifts.

Things to Make

Braided Christmas Wreaths
Card-Table House
* Child's Mirror
* Child's Telephone Book
* Christmas Candy Tree or Wreath
* Coffee Can Cookie Jar
* Collage Plaque
* Cooked Play Dough
Decorated Hand Towel
* Decorative Wastebasket
* Dough Ornaments
Drawstring Bag
Easy Candleholder

* Easy Pencil Holder
* Felt Backgammon Set
* Felt Box
Magnetic Fishing Pole
Milk Carton Candles
No-Sew Doll
Nuts-and-Bolts-of-Chess Set
* Patchwork Flower Pot
Personal Touches
Puppet Curtain
Quick Coasters
Ruffled Barrettes
* Stilts

* Item can be made easily by a child.

Braided Christmas Wreath

Select three pieces of calico, small Christmas print, or patchwork fabric with compatible colors. Piece together strips (9 in. wide by 67 in. long) of each fabric (make two strips out of one fabric for a total of four strips). Sew one strip of each fabric into a long tube. Sew one short end closed. Turn right side out and stuff loosely with polyester stuffing or used nylon hose. Blind hem other end. Hand stitch one end from each of the three tubes together. Loosely braid the tubes. Form the braid into a wreath and hand stitch the other ends so the circle keeps its shape. Make the fourth strip into a wide bow (you may need to shorten it) and attach to the top of the wreath. Sew a knitting ring at the top in the back for hanging.

Card-Table House

Measure the top of your card table. Add ⅝ in. seam allowance all around. Cut one piece of solid fabric that size. Measure the distance between the table legs

and from the floor to the top of the table. Add ⅝ in. seam allowance on all four sides. Cut four pieces of fabric that size. Decorate pieces like a playhouse, log cabin, forest, outer space, castle, etc. Cut out a window if you like and sew bias tape around the opening. Sew side pieces to top piece. Then sew side pieces together, leaving one corner open as a flap. Or cut out a door or flap and sew all side pieces together. The house will now slip easily over the top of the table for instant fantasy.

Child's Mirror

Buy a child's hand mirror with a plain plastic backing. Braid yarn and glue around top of mirror (on back) with hair. Glue on red felt circles for rouge cheeks, a red felt mouth, and false eyelashes for eyes.

Christmas Candy Tree or Wreath

Use a Styrofoam cone or wreath as your base. With straight pins, attach wrapped candies in even rows. Start at bottom so next row can overlap the pinned part.

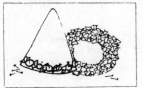

Coffee Can Cookie Jar

Thoroughly clean any size coffee can. Paint can with metal paint or cover with contact paper. Decorate with decals or painted design or personalize with tape or painted letters.

Collage Plaque

Paint or stain the edges of a wood plaque. Dry, sand with fine sandpaper, and paint again. Collect pictures, scenes, or words cut from magazines that have special meaning for the person to whom you will give the plaque. Spray the pictures on both sides with clear, acrylic fixative. Make a pleasing arrangement on the plaque and glue in place, overlapping edges and leaving no uncovered wood. Dry, then spray again with fixative. Collages are also nice on clipboards or wooden address or recipe boxes.

Cooked Play Dough

1 cup flour
½ cup salt
1 cup water

1 tablespoon vegetable oil
2 teaspoons cream of tartar
Food coloring

Mix and cook over medium heat until ball is formed. Stir constantly. Put on floured board and knead till smooth. Keep tightly covered.

Decorated Hand Towel

Buy any solid color hand towel or finger tip towel. Sew several rows of lace or trim on one end.

Decorative Wastebasket

Use any straight-sided, metal wastebasket. Cover with metal paint, contact paper, or fabric. Trim with decals, rick-rack, painted design, etc.

Dough Ornaments

1 pound baking soda
1 cup cornstarch
1¼ cups water
Food coloring (optional)

Cook in pan, stirring until it forms a ball like pie crust. Cool, then roll with rolling pin. Cut shapes with cookie cutters. Poke hole in top with toothpick. Dry overnight on cookie sheet (don't cook). Paint with felt tip pens or oil paints. Put colored ribbon or yarn through hole for hanging on Christmas tree.

Drawstring Bags

A versatile idea. Make different sizes as shoe bags for traveling; laundry bag; hair curler bag; purse; beach bag (cut top and handle off plastic bleach bottle or 1 gallon vinegar bottle to put inside bag to hold wet suit); pajama bag with pockets on outside for toothbrush, comb; tote bag for carrying toys, school supplies, needlework.

Decide the length you want the finished bag. Add 1¼ in. to the width. Double the length and add 2½ in. Cut a rectangle of material that size. (For a finished 12 × 18 bag, cut a rectangle 13¼ in. wide by 38½ long.)

Sew sides together (right sides together) using ⅝ in. seams. Sew a ¼ in. hem around top of bag. Form a casing 1 in. wide and sew, leaving about 1 in. open. Double stitch an inch on either side of opening. Thread cord or ribbon through casing and knot securely. Clip bottom corners and turn bag right side out.

Easy Candleholder

Cut desired shape (square, star, circle) from a piece of wood at least 1 in. thick. Paint, stain, or leave natural. From bottom, drive a finishing nail through center of wood, leaving a point at least 1 in. above candlestick. Stick candle over nail point.

Easy Pencil Holder

Use clean, empty frozen juice cans with no sharp edges. Spray bottom with white paint. Cover sides with fabric or Contact paper. Trim with stickers, rick-rack, ribbon, etc.

Felt Backgammon Set

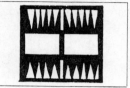

Cut one piece of felt 15 in. square for the backing. Using two contrasting colors of felt, cut 24 triangles and the lines and glue in place with fabric glue. Make a drawstring bag. Roll up the board and store with bought playing pieces in the bag.

Felt Box

Choose a flat plastic or sturdy cardboard box approximately 2 in. high with a lid. Cut circles, triangles, rectangles, letters, and odd shapes from several colors of felt for making designs. Store pieces in box. Great for children's car game or for sick-bed toy because pieces don't slide around.

Magnetic Fishing Pole

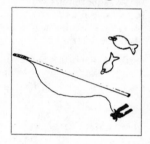

Tie 2 ft. of string onto a ¼ in. diameter dowel stick (about 18 in. long). Secure with electrician's tape. Tie small magnet onto other end of the string. Cut fish or other shapes out of construction paper, grocery sacks, light-weight material scraps, etc. Put paper clip on each shape to attract magnet.

Milk Carton Candles

Wash any size wax milk carton and cut to desired height. Fill with crushed ice and place taper candle in the middle, with wick extending above top of carton. Melt clear paraffin (about 2 cups for a quart carton) over double boiler. Color paraffin with old candle stubs or wax candles. Pour paraffin over ice. When wax is hard, pour off water and peel off carton.

No-Sew Doll

Trace a simple outline of a doll (about 6 to 10 inches tall) on ¼-inch plywood.

(If you can't draw one, you can find a simple drawing in young children's coloring books.) Cut out with a jigsaw, sand and spray with clear acrylic fixative. Paint a face with felt tip markers. Glue on yarn hair. Cut out a piece of felt to look like a body suit and glue onto doll. Now you can cut out felt tops, skirts, pants, or dresses and glue on rickrack or other trim. Felt sticks to itself; just press on, peel off.

Nuts-and-Bolts-of-Chess Set

Here's an unusual chess set you can make in an afternoon. Buy from the hardware store (or find in your garage):

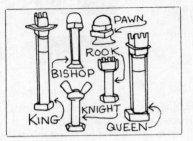

4 ⅜"×2" hex head machine bolts (or cap screws)
4 ⅜" hex nuts
2 ⅜"×2" fender nuts
8 ⅜" castle nuts
2 ⅜" standard washers
4 ⅜"×1¼" hex head machine bolts (or cap screws)
4 ⅜"×1" hex head machine bolts (or cap screws)

4 ⅜" wing nuts
16 ¼"×¾" flat head machine screws (or stove bolts)
32 ¼" square nuts
16 ¼" cap nuts
4 ¼"×1½" flat head machine screws (or stove bolts)
4 ¼" acorn nuts

Assemble the pieces in the following order (from bottom to top of each piece):

King (Make 2):   ⅜"×2" hex head machine bolt
⅜" hex nut
⅜"×½" fender nut
⅜" castle nut

Queen (Make 2): ⅜"×2" hex head machine bolt
⅜" hex nut
⅜" standard washer
⅜" castle nut

Bishop (Make 4): ¼"×1½" flat head machine screw
¼" square nut
¼" acorn nut

Knight (Make 4): ⅜"×1" hex head machine bolt
⅜" wing nut

Rook (Make 4):   ⅜" ×1¼" hex head machine bolt
⅜" castle nut

Pawn (Make 16): ¼"×¾" flat head machine screw
¼" square nut
¼" cap nut

Divide into two equal sets. Spray one set with gold spray paint and one with silver.

Seal outside of flower pot with sealer. When dry, glue small pieces of calico or bright fabric onto outside of pot and about 1 in. down top rim on inside of flower pot. Overlap pieces in random pattern, but be sure no clay is left uncovered. Spray or paint with clear fixative. You can decorate outside of pot saucer the same way.

Patchwork Flower Pot

Personal Touches

Everyone loves a personalized gift—whether it carries his name, initials, or a symbol with special meaning.

Traditional methods of personalizing include embroidery, appliqué, paint, or stencils.

Consider using some newer techniques such as iron-on's, transfers, ballpoint paints for cloth, and Wet Paint for slick surfaces such as plastic mugs, combs, headbands, boxes.

Puppet Curtain

Cut a piece of double knit or felt 5 ft. long and the width of a door opening (plus 2 in. for hem, if knit). Make a casing on top of puppet curtain for a tension rod to fit through. Hem bottom and sides if knit. Leaving 5–6 in. on each side and at least 12 in. on top, cut out a rectangle about 16 in. high for the "stage." From a contrasting light-weight material, cut a rectangle 3 in. wider and longer (plus hem allowance) than stage opening. Hem material, then sew it onto back of stage to cover stage opening. This forms the "curtain." Children hold the puppets in front of the little curtain when performing. Decorate stage as you wish and hang in doorway with tension rod.

Quick Coasters

Buy unfinished wooden coasters from hobby store. Cut out part of the design from paper doilies and glue inside coasters. Paint entire coaster including doily. When dry, spray with acrylic fixative to waterproof them.

Ruffled Barrettes

Start with a 9-inch-long strip of 1-inch-wide eyelet or lace with crocheted edging. Sew the 2 short ends together in a ¼-inch seam. Fold material over seam and stitch another seam so the first seam is hidden. Machine baste ⅛-inch from edge. Make another row of basting ⅜-inch from edge. Gather eyelet into a circle, pulling center as tight as you can. Tie off gathers.

Place circle on top of a flat plastic barrette (from dime store). Sew in place, winding thread around top of barrette. Form a 6-inch piece of ⅜-inch-wide grosgrain ribbon into a flat bow. (Don't actually tie a bow; just overlap ribbon into a bow shape.) Place center of bow over gathered center of circle. Hold a fancy button in the center of the bow and sew button and bow to ruffled circle at same time.

Stilts

Remove one end from each of two 1-pound coffee cans. With regular can opener, punch two triangular "holes" on opposite sides of coffee can top. Paint cans with metal paint. Cut two pieces of ¼-inch smooth rope, each approximately 4½ ft. long. Put one end of one rope through hole and knot (big knot) inside can. Measure a loop of rope from child's foot to his hip bone and back down, allowing 4 in. extra for knotting the other end inside the can.

Telephone Book

On a piece of construction paper, draw or paste a picture of a fireman or fire hat. In large numbers, write the number of the child's local fire department. Do the same for his doctor, police station, grandparents, his mother and father (their work numbers), or any special friends. Put only one number on a page. Punch holes on left side of paper and tie with yarn.

Appendix

Small Electric Appliances

The variety and number of small electric appliances surprised and bewildered me. Some functions they perform seem so simple by hand, I wondered why take up storage space and use costly electricity for them. Then I thought of life without my blow dryer and slow cooker and conceded the point. We all have a few favorites. I would hate to be accused of recommending one of each, but think we all deserve a little luxury in our lives.

Personal Care
Whirlpool bath
Massagers, vibrating cushion
Automatic skin refresher
Facial cleaner
Shaving cream warmer
Electric shaver
Manicure machine
Lighted make-up mirror
Portable hair dryer
Blow dryer
Curling iron
Electric curlers
Iron
Hot curling brush
Electric hair trimmer
Electric toothbrush
Facial sauna
Sunlamp
Heating pad

Serving Aids
Coffee maker—from 1 to 30 cups
Bun warmer
Portable 1 or 2 burner range
Warming tray
Plate warmer
Ice crusher

Food Preparation
Knife, knife sharpener
Can opener
Peeler
Food dehydrator
Food bag sealer
Food grinder
Peanut butter machine
Blender
Mixer—hand or on stand
Bread kneader
Juicer
Skillet
Griddle
Waffle iron
Toaster, toaster-broiler
Fry pot
Slow cooker
Crêpe maker
Doughnut maker
Cupcake, muffin maker
Pizza baker
Cookie, canapé, candy maker
Mini-oven
Hot dog cooker, burger cooker
Yogurt maker
Ice cream freezer
Popcorn popper

General Birthday Information

Symbolic Birthstones and Flowers

Month	Birthstone, *Meaning of Stone*	Flower, *Meaning of Flower*
January	Garnet, *faithfulness*	Carnation (white), *purity*
February	Amethyst, *peacemaking*	Violet, *modesty*
March	Bloodstone, *courage*	Daffodil, *welcome*
April	Diamond, *innocence*	Daisy, *innocence*
May	Emerald, *true love*	Lily of the Valley, *doubly dear*
June	Pearl	Rose (red), *love*
July	Ruby, *true friendship*	Larkspur, *lightness*
August	Sardonyx, *conjugal happiness*	Poppy, *forgetfulness*
September	Sapphire, *repentance*	Aster, *always gay*
October	Opal, *hope*	Calendula
November	Topaz, *friendship*	Chrysanthemum, *hope*
December	Turquoise, *happiness in love*	Holly, *rejoice together*

Signs of the Zodiac

Sign	Dates*	Symbol
Aries	March 21–April 20	Ram
Taurus	April 21–May 20	Bull
Gemini	May 21–June 20	Twins
Cancer	June 21–July 22	Crab
Leo	July 23–August 22	Lion
Virgo	August 23–September 22	Virgin
Libra	September 23–October 22	Scales
Scorpio	October 23–November 21	Scorpion
Sagittarius	November 22–December 21	Archer
Capricorn	December 22–January 19	Goat
Aquarius	January 20–February 18	Water Bearer
Pisces	February 19–March 20	Fish

*Dates may vary by one day depending on year of birth.

Anniversary Symbols and Gift Ideas

If you like to "go by the book," here are some ideas for gifts in each yearly category. The first group of suggested gift ideas for each anniversary is based on the traditional anniversary symbols; the second is based on the current symbols. Many more ideas are listed under *Gift Ideas: Anniversaries* or in special interest

Year Symbol: Gift Ideas

1 **Paper:** Magazine subscription, book, cookbook, stationery, photograph album, grocery bag of paper products, playing cards, tickets to special event, gift certificate, coupon for yard or housework, bridge tallies, matching party napkins and paper plates.
   Clock: Travel, alarm, kitchen, digital, kitchen timer, chiming clock, sundial.

2 **Cotton:** Matching T-shirts, shirts or nightshirts; sheets or pillowcases; placemats and napkins; cotton hammock; a crocheted ornament or item; tote bag; handmade Christmas tree skirt or stocking; throw pillow; quilt; bath set; apron; beach towel; handkerchiefs (monogrammed).
   China: Bud vase, candy dish, cup and saucer or other piece in their pattern, china flowers, china painting on a trivet or plate.

3 **Leather:** Real leather or leather-look photograph album, briefcase, wallet, belt, purse, driving gloves, luggage or luggage tag, desk accessories, coat.
   Crystal, glass: Set of glasses (see *Gift Ideas: Bar Gifts*), pitcher, hand mirror, bud vase, glass Christmas tree ornament, bottle of wine, candy dish, salt and pepper shakers (crystal), crystal coasters, glass baking dishes, stained glass window ornament, candleholders, parfait or sherbet glasses, dressing table set, or how about *liquid* crystal display (LCD) watch or calculator?

4 **Fruit, flowers, silk:** Basket of real fruit, fruit tree; dried, silk or cloth flowers, bouquet of real flowers, rose bush or other flowering plant or bulb for their garden, hanging basket or potted plant; silk pillowcases, sheets, pajamas or blouse.
   Appliances: Popcorn popper, ice cream or yogurt maker (see *Appendix: Small Appliances*).

5 **Wood:** Wooden spice rack, candleholders, bookends, picture frame, trinket box, jewelry box or valet, salad bowl set, cutting board, rocking chair, croquet set, duck decoy, golf tees; wood carving, tree for yard, piece of unfinished furniture.
   Silverware: Silver or silverplate flatware (serving piece or odd piece like iced tea spoon or grapefruit spoon in their silver pattern), tray or trivet, pendant, napkin rings, candleholders, thimble (see *Gift Ideas: Silver Gifts* for more ideas).

6 **Candy, iron:** Boxed candy; travel or steam iron; cast iron cookware, fireplace andirons or tools, trivet, hibachi, plant stand.
   Wood: See *5th Anniversary,* above.

7   **Wool, copper:** Wool blanket, sweater, scarf, caps, socks, stadium blanket; a needlepoint or knit item or a kit for her to make; afghan; copper tea kettle or cookware; knit golf club covers.
Desk sets: Pencil holder, paperweight, desk picture frame or picture of spouse or family for desk, calendar, desk organizer, bookends for desk, pen and pencil set.

8   **Bronze, pottery:** Pottery or ceramic dishware, pitcher, bowl, wind chimes, flower pot, cookie jar or jam jar; bronze door knocker or candlesticks.
Linens, laces: Linens for bed, bath, table or kitchen; linen suit; lacy lingerie, blouse, handkerchief, sachet.

9   **Pottery, willow:** See *8th Anniversary* above for pottery suggestions; willow basket.
Leather: See *3rd Anniversary,* above.

10 **Tin, aluminum:** Decorative tin box, tintype (an old kind of photograph made now in specialty shops), cookie cutters, cookie tin (full); aluminum baking pans, tennis racquet, fishing rod, step ladder, barbecue grill.
Diamond jewelry: Stick pin, watch, brooch, pendant, ring.

11 **Steel:** Stainless steel cutlery, steak knife set, cookware, pocket knife, shish kabob skewers.
Fashion jewelry: Initial, special religious or hobby symbol, neck chains, earrings.

12 **Silk, linen:** See *4th Anniversary* for silk, *8th Anniversary* for linen.
Pearls: Pearl earrings, choker; mother-of-pearl inlaid box or jewelry.

13 **Lace:** See *8th Anniversary.*
Textiles, furs: Coat, reupholster a chair or sofa, throw pillow or rug, anything handwoven, wall hanging, fur-lined gloves or slippers.

14 **Ivory:** Ivory-handled steak knives, carving set, letter opener, cocktail picks, carving.
Gold jewelry: All lengths of chains, stick pins, bracelet, ring.

15 **Crystal:** See *3rd Anniversary.*
Watch

20 **China:** It may be time to start a new set. See *2nd Anniversary.*
Platinum: Some "silver-like" jewelry is platinum.

25 **Silver:** Two silver goblets or see *Gift Ideas: Silver Gifts* or *5th Anniversary.*

30 **Pearl:** See *12th Anniversary.*
Diamond: Jewelry or diamond needle on a stereo.

35 **Coral:** Jewelry, decorative geode with vein of coral running through it, coral-colored lingerie.
Jade: The real thing or jade-colored jewelry, chess set

40 **Ruby:** Ring or earrings, ruby-red glassware, or box of ruby-red grapefruit

45 **Sapphire:** In jewelry or as a phonograph needle.

50 **Gold:** Jewelry or watch or gold coin made into a medallion.
Emerald: Jewelry or maybe something from the Emerald Isle (Ireland).

60/75 **Diamond:** Jewelry or tie tack or cuff links.

Gift Reminder Calendar

Record birthdays, anniversaries, and other gift occasions you want to remember on this calendar. Use it year after year.

You might want to use a code such as "A" for anniversary and "B" for birthday. List the year of birth or marriage and your friends will think you have a computer memory. It also makes them feel special when you remember what number anniversary it is.

For example,

Oct. 1 — Emily (B–1973)

means Emily was born Oct. 1, 1973.

Record all births on this calendar as you receive the announcements. Other dates will come up in conversation—or just ask your friends and family. They will probably tell you their birthday. Good luck learning the year!

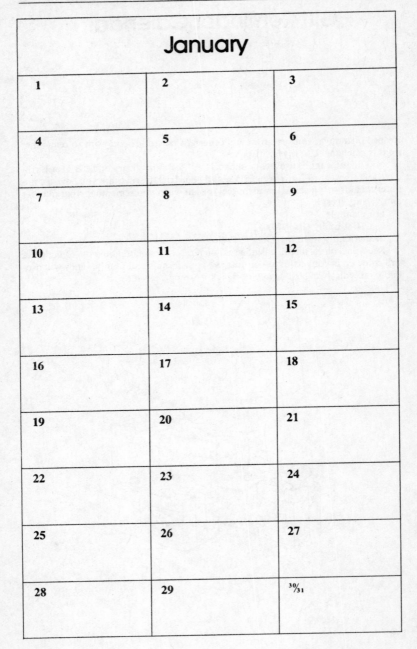

January

1	2	3
4	5	6
7	8	9
10	11	12
13	14	15
16	17	18
19	20	21
22	23	24
25	26	27
28	29	30/31

February

1	2	3
4	5	6
7	8	9
10	11	12
13	14	15
16	17	18
19	20	21
22	23	24
25	26	27
28	29	

March

1	2	3
4	5	6
7	8	9
10	11	12
13	14	15
16	17	18
19	20	21
22	23	24
25	26	27
28	29	30/31

April

1	2	3
4	5	6
7	8	9
10	11	12
13	14	15
16	17	18
19	20	21
22	23	24
25	26	27
28	29	30

May

1	**2**	**3**
4	**5**	**6**
7	**8**	**9**
10	**11**	**12**
13	**14**	**15**
16	**17**	**18**
19	**20**	**21**
22	**23**	**24**
25	**26**	**27**
28	**29**	**30/31**

June

1	2	3
4	5	6
7	8	9
10	11	12
13	14	15
16	17	18
19	20	21
22	23	24
25	26	27
28	29	30

July

1	**2**	**3**
4	**5**	**6**
7	**8**	**9**
10	**11**	**12**
13	**14**	**15**
16	**17**	**18**
19	**20**	**21**
22	**23**	**24**
25	**26**	**27**
28	**29**	**30/31**

August

1	2	3
4	5	6
7	8	9
10	11	12
13	14	15
16	17	18
19	20	21
22	23	24
25	26	27
28	29	$^{30}/_{31}$

September

1	2	3
4	5	6
7	8	9
10	11	12
13	14	15
16	17	18
19	20	21
22	23	24
25	26	27
28	29	30

October

1	2	3
4	5	6
7	8	9
10	11	12
13	14	15
16	17	18
19	20	21
22	23	24
25	26	27
28	29	$^{30}/_{31}$

November

1	2	3
4	5	6
7	8	9
10	11	12
13	14	15
16	17	18
19	20	21
22	23	24
25	26	27
28	29	30

December

1	2	3
4	5	6
7	8	9
10	11	12
13	14	15
16	17	18
19	20	21
22	23	24
25	26	27
28	29	$^{30}/_{31}$

Index

A

Addressing, packages for mailing, 15
Adult (Basic), gift ideas, 37
Animal Lovers, catalogs, 134
Animals, catalogs, 134
Animals, magazines, 118
Anniversaries, gift ideas, 39
Anniversary, gift ideas for each year, 173–174
Anniversary Information, 173–174
Anniversary Symbols, 173–174
Antique Collector, gift ideas, 40
Antiques, magazines, 118
Appendix, 171–187
Art, catalogs, 134
Artist, gift ideas, 41
Arts, magazines, 118
Audio, catalogs, 135
Audio, magazines, 123
Automobiles, magazines, 118
Aviation, catalogs, 136
Aviation, magazines, 119

B

Baby, gift ideas, 22
Bachelor, gift ideas, 42
Backgammon Set, Felt, things to make, 167
Backpacker, gift ideas, 43
Bags, Drawstring, things to make, 166
Bar Gifts, gift ideas, 45
Bar Mitzvah, gift ideas, 46
Barrettes, Ruffled, things to make, 170
Bat Mitzvah, gift ideas, 46
Beauty, catalogs, 149
Birds, catalogs, 134
Birthday Information, General, 172
Boater, gift ideas, 46
Boating, catalogs, 136
Boating, magazines, 119
Books, catalogs, 137
Bowler, gift ideas, 48
Braided Christmas Wreath, things to make, 164
Braille, magazines, 119
Bridesmaid, gift ideas, 48

C

Calendar, Gift Reminder, 175–187
Camper, gift ideas, 49
Candleholder, Easy, things to make, 166
Candlemaking, catalogs, 140
Candles, Milk Carton, things to make, 167
Card-Table House, things to make, 164
Catalogs, 133–162
Ceramics, catalogs, 140
Cheese, catalogs, 144
Chess Set, Nuts-and-Bolts-of-, things to make, 168

Children, gift ideas, 22–36
Children thru Teens, magazines, 120–121
Child's Mirror, things to make, 164
Child's Telephone Book, things to make, 165
Christmas Candy Tree or Wreath, things to make, 165
Christmas Specials, gift ideas, 51
Christmas Stocking Stuffers, gift ideas, 52
Clergy, gift ideas, 53
Clocks, catalogs, 140
Clothing, catalogs, 138
Coffee Can Cookie Jar, things to make, 165
Coffee, Tea, catalogs, 144
Collage Plaque, things to make, 165
Collector, gift ideas, 54
Collectors, catalogs, 139
Collectors, magazines, 122
College Graduation, gift ideas, 55
College Student Away From Home, gift ideas, 56
Containers, for mailing packages, 15
Cook, gift ideas, 57
Cooked Play Dough, things to make, 165
Cookie Jar, Coffee Can, things to make, 165
Craft Supplies, catalogs, 139
Crafts, gift ideas, 60
Crafts, magazines, 123
Curtain, Puppet, things to make, 169
Cushioning, for mailing packages, 15
Cycling, catalogs, 143
Cycling, magazines, 123
Cyclist, gift ideas, 62

D

Decorated Hand Towel, things to make, 165
Decorative Wastebasket, things to make, 165
Desk Dweller, gift ideas, 63
Doll, No-Sew, things to make, 167
Dough Ornaments, things to make, 166
Drawstring Bags, things to make, 166
Dried Foods, catalogs, 144

E

Easy Candleholder, things to make, 166
Easy Pencil Holder, things to make, 166
Elderly at Own Home, gift ideas, 64
Electric Appliances, Small, 171
Electronics, catalogs, 143
Electronics, magazines, 123
Eleven- to Fourteen-Year-Olds, gift ideas, 33
Enameling, catalogs, 140
Extra Special, gift ideas, 66

F

Family, gift ideas, 67
Farewell Gifts, gift ideas, 69
Felt Backgammon Set, things to make, 167
Felt Box, things to make, 167

Fifteen- to Eighteen-Year-Olds, gift ideas, 35
Fireplace Gifts, gift ideas, 70
Fish, catalogs, 134
Fisherman, gift ideas, 70
Fishing Pole, Magnetic, things to make, 167
Fitness, magazines, 126
Fitness Buff, gift ideas, 71
Flower Pot, Patchwork, things to make, 169
Food, catalogs, 143
Fruit, catalogs, 145

G
Games, magazines, 124
Games & Toys, catalogs, 160
Gardener, gift ideas, 72
Gardening, catalogs, 146
Gardening, magazines, 124
General Interest, magazines, 124
Gift Ideas, 21–116
Gift Profile, creating, 17–18
Gift Profile Form, 19–20
Gift Reminder Calendar, 175–187
Glass, catalogs, 141
Golfer, gift ideas, 73
Good Reading, magazines, 125
Gracious Living, magazines, 125
Grandparents, gift ideas, 74
Groomsman, gift ideas, 74

H
Handcrafts, catalogs, 147
Handicapped, catalogs, 148
Handicapped, gift ideas, 75
Handyman, catalogs, 148
Handyman, gift ideas, 76
Handyman, magazines, 125
Hanukkah Gifts, gift ideas, 52
Health, catalogs, 149
Health, magazines, 126
Hearing Impaired, catalogs, 149
Hearing Impaired, gift ideas, 77
Hearing Impaired, magazines, 126
Helpful Hints for Gracious Giving, 11–20
High School Graduation, gift ideas, 77
History, magazines, 126
History Buff, gift ideas, 79
Home Furnishings, catalogs, 149
Horses, magazines, 126
Host-Hostess, gift ideas, 79
Housewares, catalogs, 150
Housewarming, gift ideas, 81
Hunter, gift ideas, 83

I
Ill Persons, gift ideas, 84
Indian Supplies (Crafts), catalogs, 151
International Goods, catalogs, 151
Italian Foods, catalogs, 145

J
Jewelry, catalogs, 152
Jewelry-Making, Lapidary, catalogs, 141
Just a Little Something, gift ideas, 85

L
Leather, catalogs, 141
Lefties, catalogs, 152
Lefties, gift ideas, 86
Leisure, magazines, 124
Lifestyle, magazines, 127

M
Magazines, Special Interest, 117–132
Magnetic Fishing Pole, things to make, 167
Mailing and shipping requirements, 15
Meats, catalogs, 145
Men, gift ideas, 87
Men, magazines, 127
Mentally Ill, gift ideas, 87
Mentally Retarded, gift ideas, 88
Milk Carton Candles, things to make, 167
Miniatures & Models, catalogs, 152
Mirror, Child's, things to make, 164
Model Building, magazines, 127
Models & Miniatures, catalogs, 152
Movies, catalogs, 153
Music, catalogs, 153
Music, magazines, 127
Musician, gift ideas, 89

N
Needlework, catalogs, 141
Needleworker, gift ideas, 90
New Parents, gift ideas, 90
No-Sew Doll, things to make, 167
Nursing Home Resident, gift ideas, 91
Nuts, catalogs, 145
Nuts-and-Bolts-of-Chess Set, things to make, 168

O
One-Year-Old, gift ideas, 24
Oriental Foods, catalogs, 145
Ornaments, Dough, things to make, 166
Outdoors, catalogs, 154
Outdoors, gift ideas, 93
Outdoors, magazines, 128

P
Patchwork Flower Pot, things to make, 169
Pencil Holder, Easy, things to make, 166
Person Living Abroad, gift ideas, 95
Personal Touches, things to make, 169
Photographer, gift ideas, 96
Photography, catalogs, 156
Photography, magazines, 129
Plaque, Collage, things to make, 165
Play Dough, Cooked, things to make, 165
Pottery, catalogs, 140
Puppet Curtain, things to make, 169

Q
Quick Coasters, things to make, 169

R
Retirement Home Resident, gift ideas, 97
Ruffled Barrettes, things to make, 170
Runner, gift ideas, 98
Running, magazines, 129

S

Science, catalogs, 157
Science, magazines, 129
Scuba Diver, gift ideas, 99
Seafood, catalogs, 145
Sealing, packages for mailing, 15
Seamstress, gift ideas, 100
Seat Weaving, catalogs, 142
Shopping Guidelines, Gift, 12
Showers, Wedding, gift ideas, 112
Silver Gifts, gift ideas, 101
Single Woman, gift ideas, 101
Six- to Ten-Year-Olds, gift ideas, 29
Smorgasbord, catalogs, 157–160
Snow Skier, gift ideas, 103
Snow Sports, magazines, 130
Special Treasures, catalogs, 134
Sports, catalogs, 154
Sports, magazines, 130
Sports Fan, gift ideas, 103
Stationery, catalogs, 160
Stilts, things to make, 170
Stocking Stuffers, gift ideas, 52
Sweets, catalogs, 145

T

Tea, Coffee, catalogs, 144
Teacher, gift ideas, 104
Telephone Book, Child's, things to make, 170
Tennis Player, gift ideas, 105
Things to Make, 163–170
Three- to Five-Year-Olds, gift ideas, 26
Towel, Decorated Hand, things to make, 165
Toys, Guide to Buying, 13
Toys & Games, catalogs, 160
Travel, magazines, 131

Traveler, gift ideas, 105
Tree or Wreath, Christmas Candy, things to make, 165
Two-Year-Old, gift ideas, 25
Typewriters, catalogs, 161

U

United Parcel Service mailing requirements, 15
U.S. Postal Service, domestic rates, 16
U.S. Postal Service, mailing requirements, 15
U.S. Postal Service, size standards, 16

V

Vegetarian, gift ideas, 108
Vehicles, magazines, 118
Video, magazines, 123
Visually Impaired, catalogs, 162
Visually Impaired, gift ideas, 108

W

Wastebasket, Decorative, things to make, 165
Water Skier, gift ideas, 110
Water Sports, magazines, 131
Weaving, catalogs, 142
Wedding, gift ideas, 110
Wedding Showers, gift ideas, 112
Western, catalogs, 162
Western, gift ideas, 113
Wildlife, magazines, 118
Women, gift ideas, 114
Women, magazines, 131
Woman, Single, gift ideas, 101
Wood Hobbyist, gift ideas, 115
Woodworking, catalogs, 142
Wrapping Ideas, Gift, 14
Writer, gift ideas, 116
Writing, magazines, 132

Reader's Digest Fund for the Blind is publisher of the Large Type Edition of *Reader's Digest.* **For further information about the special edition, please contact Reader's Digest Fund for the Blind, Inc., Dept. 250, Pleasantville, NY 10570.**